WITHDRA

The Shipbuilders

The
SHIPBUILDERS

From Clipper Ships
to Submarines to Hovercraft

D. S. HALACY, Jr.

J. B. Lippincott Company

PHILADELPHIA *and* NEW YORK

Four Girls Memorial Library
Pembroke Academy

Copyright © 1966 by D. S. Halacy, Jr.

Printed in the United States of America

Library of Congress Catalog Card Number 66–10886

FIRST EDITION

*To the memory of my father—
who was a sailor.*

4

Foreword

In an age of jet aircraft, nuclear power, and spaceflight, it is refreshing and perhaps comforting to look back on man's simpler conquest of the sea. Beyond the pleasure of reliving the exciting adventure of ships and the men who built them, however, is a lesson applicable to man's continuing projects: a worthy goal is, in itself, no guarantee of success. Instead it seems that the greatest accomplishments are achieved only after the most dedicated and sacrificing perseverance on the part of those who believe. This story of man's struggle against one of the elements, then, is but a glimpse of the whole battle. We contend with an environment that includes ourselves.

Spanning as it does a period of many centuries, the book required research in places ranging from ancient history to current technical publications and news releases. For all these sources I am grateful. In particular I am indebted for pleasant and helpful visits with the staff at Mystic Seaport, Connecticut, and Librarian Theda Bassett and her "crew" at the U. S. Naval Submarine Base, New London—Groton, Connecticut.

D. S. H.

July, 1965

Contents

"Surely oak and threefold brass surrounded his heart
who first trusted a frail vessel to the merciless ocean."
—Horace

Introduction

Of all the many modes of transportation, no other has the vital and romantic place in man's progress as that earned by the ship. We have but to study history and geography, or scan the pages of literature to appreciate the great importance of sailing craft through the years. Ships did much to shape the destiny of the world and the characters of men. In this book we shall meet some great builders of ships, against the exciting backdrops of the age they lived in, and learn why and how they created the vessels they are famed for.

The first "boat" must have been discovered when some drowning Paleolithic man grabbed in desperation at a floating log and found that it would sustain his weight until he could struggle to shore. From this happy accident man learned to cross deep streams clinging to his "life preserver," and even to float downstream upon it.

Later, a pioneer sailor lashed two or more logs together and sat high and dry upon them instead of floating in the water. Others substituted bundles of reeds for the logs, or even the inflated bladders of animals. Man discovered that he could push himself along with a pole, or even "paddle" with it or his hands: no longer did he have to float at the whim of the current. Next came the discovery of the sail and the power of the wind, probably by someone clad in voluminous garments that flapped in the breeze and caught sufficient wind to propel sailor, boat, and all along with it!

How early it was that man built boats we cannot be sure, since wood is not durable enough to be preserved down through the ages. But the Bible tells of the giant Ark, some 450 feet long, that Noah used to save humans and animals from the Flood. Egyptians had sailing craft as early as 2600 B.C. In about 1500 B.C. Queen Hatshepsut of Egypt sent not one ship but a fleet of them on an exploratory voyage to the "land of Punt" far to the south, possibly somewhere in Africa. This sea journey lasted several years and was a highly successful forerunner of voyages that would one day circumnavigate the globe.

No longer were ships restricted to rivers, lakes, or the waters close to shore; they could now sail boldly out to sea far beyond sight of land. Maritime trade built great civilizations by carrying to and fro not only material things but ideas as well. The ship was early a weapon of war, used to prey on other ships and even to subjugate whole peoples.

Great slave galleys of the Greeks and Romans swept the seas for hundreds of years, and heroic voyages like those of Odysseus and Jason inspired early literature.

Far to the north the Vikings of the Scandinavian countries ranged the seas both as explorers and conquerors. They descended on Europe and the British Isles, and even sailed far west to strange new lands. A few hundred years later, Columbus, too, steered his three small vessels toward the fearful "edge of the world" and found not the trade route he sought, but a New World.

During the sixteenth century, ships flowered under the reign of Henry VIII. The giant warship *Great Harry*, mounting an incredible total of 186 guns, typified the growing maritime strength of tiny England, whose ships would create an empire on which the sun would not set for hundreds of years. Sir Francis Drake sailed another famous ship around the world, provoking the Spanish until they built the huge Armada that met England in 1588 for the greatest defeat ever suffered by a nation at sea.

Ships were a primary cause of the rise and fall of empires, and it was the tiny *Mayflower* that in 1620 carried a band of Pilgrims to freedom in America. Later, ships would bring slaves as well, and colonizers from other lands. Back in Europe, wars still raged and in the eighteenth century Lord Nelson's great *Victory* was a fighting ship in the tradition of the craft laid down by Henry VIII two hundred years earlier. Another Englishman, Captain Cook, carried the flag to distant lands with his *Endeavour*.

We begin our story in the nineteenth century, when the age of sail makes a last valiant stand against the invasion of the marine steam engine. In perhaps ten thousand years, shipbuilding had progressed from crudely hollowed logs paddled by the sailor's hands to fleet craft capable of carrying themselves and great loads of goods around the world. The next century and a half would see a fantastically accelerated progress, one that began first in the keen minds of a handful of imaginative shipbuilders.

There is a saying that if a man builds a better mousetrap the world will beat a path to his door but the idea does not seem to apply to inventions of seagoing nature. Perhaps a better rattrap would have met a good reception in the wooden ships of old but ideas for new *ships* were resisted with ferocity by the seafaring men to whom they were presented. Almost without exception, the men responsible for the revolutions that took place on the water were subjected to ridicule, abuse, financial reverses, and failure. It was to be expected that some would drown in their ships. Some even took their own lives in despair and frustration. The miracle of progress in shipbuilding is not one of ideas alone, but of the hardheadedness with which these men of ideas were endowed. They are owed a debt seldom paid within their lifetimes. Yet time after time they persevered in the face of all adversity and sailed their new creations across the seven seas. We can be thankful that they did.

The Shipbuilders

> "It was of another form, indeed;
> Built for freight, and yet for speed,
> A beautiful and gallant craft—"
>
> —Henry Wadsworth Longfellow,
> *The Building of the Ship*

I

Donald McKay—

Master Clipper Builder

CLIPPER: *a fast sailing ship; esp: one with long slender lines, and overhanging bow, tall raking masts, and a large sail area.*

It may seem odd that we shall begin this book with an ending, the last brief flaring of sails on the sea. But an ending may be a beginning too, and the end of the age of sail merged with the birth of steam as power for ships. By 1850 the doom of the sailing vessel was all but sealed, and yet in the next decade or two there occurred one of the most amazing resurgences of an idea in the history of the sea.

There are the legends of the "swan song" in which the dying bird finds beautiful voice to serenade the world it is leaving. Less nautical but more factual is the nova, or bursting sun that in dying provides a cosmic spectacle to thrill astronomers vast distances away. So it was with sailing ships. They went out with a blaze of rushing glory, in an age both romantic and challenging—the age of the clipper ships. What spacecraft and astronauts are to us today, so were the clipper ships and sailors a hundred and more years ago. Newspapers were filled with their exploits and adventuresome youngsters dreamed of putting to sea aboard a sleek "extreme clipper" boasting two acres of sail and a hull that fairly streaked through the green billowing foam. This was a craft so beautiful it made throats ache to see it; so perfect that some writers have called its design and building the American equivalent of old-world fine art. In the words of historian Samuel E. Morison: "*Flying Cloud* was the long-suppressed artistic impulse of a practical, hardworked race. *Flying Cloud* was our Rheims."

There was more than beauty, of course. The world was on the edge of an age of speed, and the clipper ship showed its heels to all challengers then on the sea. How fast could a sailing ship travel? The *Sovereign of the Seas* hurtled across 424 nautical miles—equivalent to more than 475 of the land miles we are more familiar with—in a single twenty-four-hour period. This was an average of eighteen knots, a speed that steamships would not match for decades to come, and the clipper ship achieved such a journey without the expenditure of a single lump of coal or pint of resin burned under a boiler. No dirty smoke smudged the skies of clipper days; no din of pounding engines hammered at decks and smote the ears. There was instead only the clean sound of wind in tall rigging and the hiss of the sea sliced by a knifelike bow.

Small wonder the clipper ship was a symbol in the middle of the last century and remains today a proud synonym for fast jet aircraft—clipper ships of the sky. So bold was the concept of the clipper ship that men of less vision mercilessly taunted their brothers who staked fortunes and reputations on those sleek and narrow hulls, those towering banks of sail upon sail that surely seemed too much for a single ship to carry. The clippers appeared on the sea just before 1850. By 1875, they were all but gone. Today there is only *one* such craft left for the world to see: Britain's proud *Cutty Sark*, preserved at Greenwich much as she was at the height of her grandeur. For the rest, there is only the memory of ships like *Flying Cloud* and *Rainbow*, *Stag Hound* and *Sovereign of the Seas*. And of men like Donald McKay, surely the foremost practitioner of the fine art of designing and building clipper ships. The age of the clipper is long past, but the heritage remains for all who will claim it. It is a proud and thrilling legacy.

· *Reason for the Clippers*

The clipper ship did not just happen, anymore than space satellites just happened. A number of factors contributed to make that period of history right for the flowering of the new craft. A hundred years ago the sea was of great importance to Americans. Proof of this lies in the fact that there were some thirty thousand sailing vessels operating from American ports, giving livelihood to perhaps one-third of a million seamen, to say nothing of the others connected in various ways with the maritime world. There were dozens of different occupations, from the shipper of goods to the carver of artistic figureheads for sailing vessels; from the insurance agent to the spinner of cloth that would become a sail.

Military strength was measured in sea power. Commercial goods and human cargo had to move by sea—even to go from New York to San Francisco it was preferable to board a ship rather than attempt a land crossing. European emigrants came to America in the holds of ships; so did the priceless tea from China, and the infamous opium smuggled to China. The surface of the earth consists mainly of water, and to get from place to place meant crossing much of that water.

For centuries speed had been either of no consideration, or an unattainable dream of the seafarer. The ocean could angrily kick up its heels, and ships were designed mostly with safety in mind. Speed was of lesser importance. It was a strange fact that early English taxes actually favored slower cargo craft and the companies with a monopoly on shipping cared little for fast service because there was no competition.

In the nineteenth century things slowly began to change, however. The East India Company lost its charter, and competition reared its head among the other shippers who sought to dominate the sea lanes. Trade, both of human and cargo goods, prompted the idea of regular service rather than the age-old tradition of sailing only when a full hold was achieved and the weather looked right. Shippers and passengers were ripe for a service that would sail on a regular schedule. In 1815 the famous Black Ball line began such a service back and forth across the Atlantic with fast new packet ships. Thus began a revolution on the seas; a revolution keyed to industrial revolution in England and political revolution and independence in America. In time the industrial revolution would emerge as the more important motivation, and put an end to sail. But for now there was the opening long awaited by the handful of Yankees who dreamed of sailing ships that would show their heels to the crawling craft of the British, for so long rulers of the sea.

Traditionally those British ships, and the American vessels patterned after them, were built along the lines of a tub. Their bows were as round as the puffing cheeks of the North wind that drove them scudding across the waves. Their hulls had "tumble-home" sides, for that was the philosophy of their design. Safety was the keynote, and the walnut-shell craft did tumble home voyage after voyage.

The East India Company craft also sailed on a like safety principle. Under full sail they might reach speeds of ten or maybe even twelve knots. But suppose a gale came up? Therefore, the standard procedure was to reef sails in the evening and proceed at a fraction of the speed possible. If bad weather came, the skipper was prepared.

America was aided in its battles with the mother country by the fact that it had little of anything to begin with, including ships. A nation of rebels, it was called, and there were rebels among its naval architects. In the War of 1812, American-built packets and privateers sailed rings about the traditionally built British craft. England was at a handicap. She had all those old craft that were admittedly slower but what could she do about them? Surely they could not be sunk. Neither could they be speeded up greatly. So the

British plowed along with slower craft simply because they had them. America had to build new vessels, and in the process made them faster. Even if comfort was sacrificed, Americans still did not mind, in the only slightly exaggerated words of a French writer, "sailing with their feet in the water"!

Baltimore, Maryland, was a center of shipbuilding activity during the war, and among the craft plying the waters of Chesapeake Bay when hostilities ended were speedy packets, as well as small craft used as pilot boats. In 1832 there appeared a vessel some historians call the first of the clipper ships. She was the *Ann McKim*, built in Baltimore for shipper Isaac Webb. Others say the *Ann McKim* was a step in the right direction, but not yet a true clipper. Here we run into the problem of definitions. What did "clipper" mean anyhow? Perhaps simply a ship that clipped through the waves, although the term may have come from the description of fast-stepping racehorses; horses that clipped time from the record books. Another theory is that clipper stems from "*klepper*," a word of Pennsylvania Dutch origin used to describe such horses. In any event American vessels surely showed their heels to the slower thoroughbreds of England, and so the term found favor.

Whether or not *Ann McKim* was truly a clipper, she did inspire what all acknowledge to be clipper ships. For some time there had been ship designers who wanted to break away from the fat, tumble-home sides and bluff bows of existing craft. They wanted sleeker hulls, plus more canvas to drive those hulls faster through the water. Tradition is a strong force, however, and for years these dreamers had to build compromises between their new ideas and more conventional craft which would please the shippers who wanted to continue the way their fathers had before them. The *Ann McKim*, with her speed, gave new courage and hope.

New York's shipbuilding community had not yet deserted tradition, but there were a few rebels ready to do so. Among them were men like John Griffiths, Nat Palmer, and Donald McKay. It was a tough battle, and they fought against ingrained ideas like Isaac Newton's dictum that the ideal ship had a "codfish head and a mackerel tail," and that her length should be no more than three times her breadth for least resistance. But the *Ann McKim* was much more than three times as long as she was broad. The more Griffiths and McKay studied the flight of birds and the swimming of fish, the more they ached to build a new design. Griffiths gave lecture after lecture and showed models he and McKay had tested in primitive water-tank tests. It would be Griffiths' good fortune to build the first real clipper; Donald McKay had been forced to leave New York and move to Boston for work.

In 1843 Griffiths convinced the firm of Howland and Aspinwall, who were sailing the *Ann McKim* profitably, despite the dire predictions of their colleagues, that he could build them an even faster ship using his radical new ideas. Two years later he launched the first of the clipper ships, *Rainbow*. It took that long because of the talk about "Aspinwall's folly," and the resultant doubts that crept into the owners' minds. They called in European consultants, and worried and fretted and delayed. But in the end, *Rainbow* was completed and she slid down the ways into an icy East River in January of 1845. With her launching came the era of the wonderful clipper ship; yet she was hailed by learned experts as a freak craft that would surely plough her way to the bottom of the sea if any skipper was foolhardy enough to leave port in her!

Ann McKim had been a rakish enough craft. With a beam of 31 feet, she was 143 feet from bow to stern, a ratio of some 4½ to 1. *Rainbow* was also 31 feet in beam, but nearly 160 feet long! Here was a ratio of more than 5 to 1! Nor was that all that was wrong with her in the eyes of mossback critics. Conventional bows were curved outward, round as apples. *Rainbow* had concave bows that actually curved inward, something like the hollow grinding of a razor. This was what caused the dire predictions that she would slice her way to the bottom of the sea. That, cried the critics, was no bow. It was really a stern. And with all that sail—well, she'd never reach Sandy Hook. But to the surprise of all except John Griffiths, and Donald McKay, waiting eagerly for news up in Boston, *Rainbow* sailed clear to Hong Kong in the amazing time of ninety-two days, and then returned in only eighty-eight with a load of prime tea! Now McKay, the young Nova Scotian, was destined to build his own clipper ships.

· *Donald McKay*

Except for the misfortune of birth, Donald McKay might have been builder of the first clipper. He was born in 1810, in Shelbourne, Nova Scotia, of a proud Scottish family. There was nobility in his lineage but in the nineteenth century the McKays were scratching hard on a stony farm to stay alive. When Donald and his brother Lauchlan wanted to do some fishing to help out the hungry family there was no boat for them to sail, so they rebuilt an abandoned hulk. Here was Donald's first contact with shipbuilding, and the experience fired something deep inside him.

The boy might have found work close to home, but he had heard of the great ships being built in ports like New York. So, as things at home went from bad to worse, in 1826 young Donald sailed to New York to try to find a living there.

His first job was as apprentice in the shipyard of Isaac Webb, working fifteen hours a day, six days a week for the princely wage of almost nine cents an hour. By the early 1830's the shaggy Nova Scotian was working as a ship-builder for nearly double that wage, and with hours cut to a leisurely ten a day there was time for evening studies of theory and design. Naturally he met architect John Griffiths and Nat Palmer and the three of them planned and dreamed and tested their ideas in tanks of water. Palmer was a sailing captain; he knew ships and had keen ideas on how they should be designed.

In 1833 Donald McKay married Albenia Boole, daughter of a shipbuilder. He had long ago decided that his career would be as a builder of ships rather than as a merchant or a sea captain, even though he might have succeeded in either of these endeavors and the rewards were far greater. He seemed on his way to fame and fortune when his abilities led to a foreman's job at the Brooklyn Navy Yard. But his hopes were shortlived. The Americans he bossed took unkindly to the young Nova Scotian; he was a foreigner to them, and they wanted no part of him. In the end a bitter McKay quit and moved to Maine where a man could succeed on his ability rather than his birth.

There were other moves, and finally McKay went to East Boston as partner in a shipbuilding firm. The *Joshua Bates* which he built there was a packet ship that would lead to Enoch Train's famous White Diamond Line of Boston-Liverpool craft.

By 1845 McKay was in business for himself in Boston, with a fine home on White Street for his family. Had it not been for the difficulty in Brooklyn, Donald would doubtless have been building clippers by this time. But he was doing well with more conventional packets and his brother Lauchlan, with whom he had built his first ship long years ago in Shelbourne, was among the many who advised him to stay with this kind of construction. So in 1845 it was the packet *Washington Irving* for Enoch Train that left the ways of the McKay shipyard at the foot of Border Street.

In 1846 the *Anglo-Saxon* and *New World* were launched in time to enter the brisk trade prompted by the terrible Irish potato famine. *Ocean Monarch* and the *A.Z.* were built in 1847, and 1848 saw three McKay packets launched, the *Anglo-American*, the *L.Z.* and the *Jenny Lind*, named for the famous "Swedish Nightingale" who was then charming American audiences. In 1849 there were four more McKay packets launched and the pace quickened even more in 1850 when McKay built five packets and one other ship. That other ship was the first McKay clipper, *Stag Hound*.

In 1849 gold was discovered in California. This gave impetus to McKay's long smoldering desire to build one of the radical new ships. Men clamored for passage to the West, and quick passage at that. Cargo brought fabulous prices in the booming city of San Francisco where crews deserted to pan gold and get rich, and ships were beached and turned into bunkhouses and curio shops. So many ships were built for the trade that there was talk of "running out of timber back home."

John Griffiths' *Rainbow* had boasted a revolutionary slenderness of hull; *Stag Hound* was even sleeker. Her beam was less than 40 feet and yet she measured almost 210 feet from stem to stern. With a registered tonnage of 1,534, she was the largest merchant ship afloat. A bottle of rum was smashed against her bow on an icy day in December of 1850 and the first extreme clipper ship to be built in Boston was launched. Her figurehead was a panting stag hound, perhaps suggesting McKay's eagerness to catch up with John Griffiths and his five-year lead. Was he really chasing a rainbow, he must have wondered, as the sleek craft with her towering load of canvas—eleven thousand square yards of it—sailed down the harbor.

Old-timers stared in horror at the bow of *Stag Hound*. Where his earlier packets had bows that were still rounded out like apples, lunatic Donald McKay had turned his new craft "inside out"! It was against nature, they cried in protest. So ingrained was this concept of ship design that British firms who later acquired a McKay clipper would round out her knifelike front end with false planking. For his part, McKay would call them "Liverpool butchers" and make his next clipper even "sharper."

Despite the success of *Rainbow* and other clippers, there were still many who predicted that the more knifelike

Stag Hound would bury herself in the first big wave she met and founder. Insurance underwriters were among these pessimists, and they charged Sampson and Tappan, her owners, extra premiums as *Stag Hound* loaded her first cargo.

On February 1, less than two months from her launching, *Stag Hound* sailed for California under Captain Josiah Richardson. Six days at sea a roaring wind tore away her mainmast and three topgallant masts. Yet 51 days later Captain Richardson would be writing a letter from Valparaiso, Chile, to the ship's owners saying in part that he was in love with *Stag Hound*, and that the ship was yet to be built that could beat her. Despite all the troubles of that maiden voyage she still reached San Francisco in 108 days. From there she went to Manila, Canton, and back home to New York with a load of precious tea. She had set no records for speed but her performance was a credit to McKay and to the foresight of the merchants who bought her. This first voyage, of less than eleven months, resulted in profit enough to pay her cost and leave an additional $80,000 for her owners!

On her second trip, under Captain C. F. W. Behm, *Stag Hound* had the misfortune of being becalmed for 20 days on the west coast, yet still reached San Francisco in 124 days. She raced the ship *Sea Serpent* to Whampoa for tea and won by 9 days. Loaded with the valuable cargo, she sped back to New York in 95 days.

Captain Richardson had said the ship to beat *Stag Hound* was yet to be built, but even as he wrote those lines Donald McKay had another clipper under construction that would make *Stag Hound* seem slow by comparison. *Stag Hound* had been but 60 days from design to launching. His second clipper was likewise produced in record time. On April 15, 1851, *Flying Cloud*, the most famous clipper ship ever built, slid down the ways. She had been ordered by Enoch Train, who had bought so many of the McKay packets for his lines, but the firm of Grinnell, Minturn, & Co. bought her before she was finished for the grand sum of $90,000, twice what she cost Train. A number of merchants had bid on her and Train, seeing a sure profit, had sold. He would rue that decision for the rest of his life.

With a displacement of 1,783 tons, *Flying Cloud* was the new giant of the shipping world. She was undoubtedly the leanest craft afloat, too, measuring some 235 feet in length and only 41 in the beam. Her bow was more knifelike than ever and again the doomsayers predicted that now surely Donald McKay would get his comeuppance.

On June 3, 1851, *Flying Cloud* sailed from New York with Captain Josiah Cressy commanding. Mrs. Cressy was aboard, too, as she was on all his voyages. She was no mere passenger but served as navigator. The voyage was to prove hardly a fitting one for a lady. As with *Stag Hound*, gales carried away sails and mast. A disgruntled sailor bored holes in the ship and the forecastle was flooded before his sabotage was discovered. Around the horn, rain, sleet, and heavy snow made things worse. Yet on July 31 Mrs. Cressy's sights showed that *Flying Cloud* had covered the fantastic distance of 374 nautical miles in a single day.

Just out of San Francisco, the clipper lost her fore topgallant mast, but there was no stopping her now. When she anchored off North Beach in San Francisco Harbor, *Flying Cloud* was only eighty-nine days, twenty-one hours out of

New York. She had broken all the records in the book, and that on her maiden voyage! When she sailed triumphantly home in ninety-four days from Canton, there was dancing in the streets. Her owners feted Cressy and printed the log of the famous ship on white silk with gold ink. History had been made, and Donald McKay smiled proudly with the satisfaction of a man who had known all along that his ideas were right.

Soon after *Flying Cloud* thrilled the world with its speed and beauty, Donald McKay began construction of another clipper to make *Stag Hound* and *Flying Cloud* seem small. She was to be *Sovereign of the Seas* in more than name. The new clipper was 265 feet long with a beam of 44 feet, pushing the ratio to an unbelievable 6 to 1, or double that of Newton's classical formula. She was expected to carry three thousand tons of cargo.

Lauchlan McKay had counseled against the building of clippers in the McKay yards, but it was Captain Lauchlan McKay who took the *Sovereign* on her maiden voyage to San Francisco. Fully loaded, and with twenty-one passengers and a crew of 105, she sailed on August 4, 1852, a poor time of year for a quick trip. From oceanographer Lieutenant Matthew Maury, the captain learned that if he did a perfect job of sailing he could reach the Pacific Equator in 83 days, and San Francisco in 103.

Enoch Train, who had sadly seen the *Flying Cloud* prove him wrong in selling her off, was the owner of the *Sovereign*, counting on Donald McKay's skill to make him a fine profit on the giant of the seaways. But there must have been some qualms in the merchant as he watched his huge investment disappear over the horizon that late summer day.

The *Sovereign* crossed the Equator in the Atlantic in twenty-five days, the fastest time ever made by a sailing ship in August. She rounded Cape Horn and sailed back up along the west coast of South America. Off Valparaiso, where the *Stag Hound* had put in for repairs, the *Sovereign* lost her maintopmast, foretopsail yard, and mizzen top-gallant mast. Besides this, the wind ripped every bit of sail from her mainmast. By the following day the debris had been cleared from the decks and the ship was proceeding at about two-thirds speed on what sail she had left. Then, as she sailed, Captain Lauchlan supervised the re-rigging. On the 80th day the ship had been completely re-rigged, and was again coasting northward at top speed. She crossed the Pacific Equator on the very day predicted by Maury, and on the 103rd day she sailed into San Francisco Harbor! Her best day's run for the trip had been 368 nautical miles.

The *Sovereign* made a profit on her cargo of nearly $100,000, justifying the faith of Train in his shipbuilder. From then on the ship continued to be a successful merchantman. On March 18, 1853, she logged the greatest distance ever traveled by a sailing ship in a single day: 424 nautical miles (almost 485 "statute" or land miles). For eleven days the *Sovereign* averaged 330 miles a day. A year later, under a German skipper, the ship reportedly sailed 410 nautical miles in a day, and hit the unbelievable speed of twenty-two knots (almost 25 miles per hour). The 424-mile record was never equaled.

The *Sovereign* was only one of seventy-two clippers

launched in the year 1852. The shipping business had flourished, aided by the gold discovery in California, and later in Australia. Tea, and less admirably, the opium trade, provided more reason for building faster ships, and hundreds of sleek merchantmen roved the globe. Of them all, the great clippers of Donald McKay were the toast of the maritime world, and the center of even the landlubbers' attention. In all, eleven ships had sailed from New York to San Francisco in less than ninety days. All but two of these fast voyages were made by McKay ships, and *Flying Cloud* did the trick twice.

Along with the new breed of shipbuilders, men like McKay, Griffiths, and the others, appeared a new kind of skipper. A dashing combination of jet airliner captain and hot-rodder, the clipper captain drove his ship as a jockey does a horse. The clippers, or *"kleppers,"* were really that: high-stepping seahorses, driven for the last bit of speed in them. Builders piled sail onto sail, until one sailor jokingly described the canvas reaching heavenward: "Skysail, main moonraker, stargazer, skyscraper, and angel's footstool!" Another swore his skipper even ran up his long-handled drawers to the top of the mast. Those topmost bits of canvas were more a challenge to the angry wind than motive power; they typified the hard-driving captains who lashed their chairs to the deck and spent days with their eyes aloft.

This was the age of the skippers nicknamed "Bully" for their harsh tactics. Among them was Bully Waterman, skipper of *Sea Witch,* one of the early clippers to California. Waterman is said to have "padlocked the rigging" so that fearful sailors could not reef any sails no matter how terrible the gales. It is doubtful that he actually did this, nailed the sheets to the yard, as some claimed, or shot balky sailors out of the rigging. He was a fearful driver, however, and in San Francisco once had to flee a lynch mob of sailors. He and his mate were brought to trial in California for deaths in his crew but they got clean bills of health.

Other skippers, pushing their ships every bit as fast, nevertheless treated their crews with kindness and more. On one voyage of the *Flying Cloud*, Mrs. Cressy saw a seaman washed overboard in a storm. Captain Cressy immediately slowed the ship and put out boats for hours until miraculously the man was found in the heavy sea and saved. Regardless of the humanity or its lack in a captain, the clippers took a terrific pounding from the sea and the wind. Few reached their destination with the same mast and sails they set out with.

American ships were built mostly of soft woods instead of the teak British builders used and they were destined not to last. Slowly they grew waterlogged and rode lower and lower in the water. It was almost as though the gallant ships knew that clipper days were numbered, although in the halcyon days of the 1850's all denied it and derided the competition of steam.

• *The Coming of the End*

As early as 1853 steam was writing its challenge on the waters. On June 18 of that year the triumphant *Sovereign* set sail from New York to Liverpool, numbering among her passengers Donald McKay and his wife. Departing at about the same time was the steamship *Canada* and natu-

Four Girls Memorial Library

Pembroke Academy

rally the event turned into a race. During the first five days *Sovereign* turned in a best day's run of some 340 miles, while *Canada* could only do 306. So fleet was the giant sailing ship that she was 325 miles in the lead! Steam? Donald McKay laughed. Steam was fit only for machinery to build ships with, or at best to power harbor tugs. Sail was supreme for ocean voyages, and here was proof.

Sovereign plunged on to the east, reaching Liverpool in less than fourteen days for a new sailing ship mark. But there was disappointment in spite of this performance; *Canada* had docked two days earlier when the winds for the last part of the voyage slackened and slowed the *Sovereign*. Steam was more than just a smoky smudge on the horizon.

In 1853 Donald McKay built what was surely the largest of the clippers in the *Great Republic*. Three hundred and thirty-five feet long and nearly 50 feet in the beam, she was registered at more than 4500 tons. Even the huge *Sovereign* was registered at only a bit over 2400 tons. But tragedy struck this new queen of the seas—for whom McKay had declined an offer of $300,000—as she lay in New York awaiting her maiden voyage to England with a full cargo. Fire broke out in a ship anchored near the *Republic*, and when morning came the noble clipper was burned almost to the waterline. A grieving Donald McKay came down from Boston to see the wreck and turn her over to the insurance underwriters. He could not take her back for rebuilding, and another shipyard took on that task.

Rebuilt to a size far smaller than her original design, the *Republic* nevertheless acquitted herself nobly. On her first trip to Liverpool her captain claimed she made the voyage land to land in twelve days. But she was so huge there was no dock that could take her. Except for the Crimean War, and French need of a large troop transport, the *Republic* might have been laid up in England a long time waiting for a proper cargo. She was still a giant in size. She served in that war, and again in the Civil War in America. Finally, in 1872, she went down in a storm near Bermuda.

The *Great Republic* was the last of the big clippers and 1854 saw the building of the last of the "extreme" clippers of any size. Slowly, new clippers ceased to be built.

In 1859 *Sovereign* ran aground in the Straits of Malacca and broke up, but *Stag Hound* was still going strong despite her soaked timbers in 1860. In that year she raced the steamer *Atlantic* across the ocean to London with a copy of Lincoln's inaugural address and won. For this feat her skipper was awarded a prize by publisher James Gordon Bennett. The following year, a load of coal in her hold caught fire and gallant *Stag Hound* burned and sank off Brazil.

The clippers were dying off already, despite the refusal of the clipper men to face that fact. Gold had played out. Typical of the comedown of the great ships was the fate of the *Sea Witch*, once the star of the California run. Loaded with Chinese coolies she sank approaching the Indies, her waterlogged hull finally giving up the fight.

Wooden ships were on the way out; what of iron hulls with sails? Some were built, but sails were doomed, too. Flying before the wind, the sailing vessel was still giving the steamer a battle on the run from Britain to the East. But in 1864 a Frenchman named de Lesseps dealt the ships a cruel cut by completing the Suez Canal. Now steamships could lop months from the journey by sailing in an almost direct line from east to west rather than half around the world. Sailing vessels could not negotiate the canal, and so could not compete profitably.

The tragedy of the American Civil War in 1863 was a tragedy for sailing ships, too. The merchant fleet suffered a death blow, and when it was time to replace them, most of the new ships would be steam-powered. Even McKay, who had brought the great art of sailing ship construction to its highest flowering, gave up to change in the end. During the Civil War he constructed two warships for the United States Navy—ships of iron and steam. He also launched two merchant steamers.

In 1874 the gallant *Flying Cloud* burned at dockside. A year later McKay retired, moving to a farm much like the one on which he had spent his boyhood. In 1880, as the last of the proud sailing ships were vanishing from the face of the seas they had conquered, Donald McKay, too, passed from this world. Yet he had left his mark.

• *An Appraisal*

Fortunes were made and lost with wagers placed on races by the great clippers. There was keen competition between the British and the American upstarts, with the latter usually winning. It is true that Donald McKay and John Griffiths proved with their great clippers that it was possible to reach speeds of twenty knots with sail. But it should be remembered that the clippers were not simply high-speed racing yachts, playthings for their hard-driving skippers and owners, or racehorses of the sea. The clippers were merchantmen first and foremost. Although their speed and daring was romantic, their greatest success was as efficient transports. The rest was but a bonus.

Man's first boats and ships were powered craft; powered by the oars of crews or slaves. Sail superseded muscle power and made ships romantic vessels that sailed the seas on energy provided by nature, and looked loftily down at such craft as were still dragged through the water by main strength and awkwardness. Who could foresee that one day another kind of power would likewise oust sail from its position of leadership?

In England the steam engines of Watt and others first worked in the mines pumping water, once the chore of horses. But by the late eighteenth century "lunatic inventors" were trying to put the clumsy steam engines in boats. Fulton succeeded in 1807, three years before Donald McKay was born. There had been other outlandish ideas demonstrated; the undersea boat, for instance. Such things as submarines and steamships would remain awkward freaks of the sea, thought sailing men. And so it seemed. Even when Samuel Cunard managed scheduled steamship voyages across the Atlantic, sails continued to show him their sterns and to make the journey with no bulky fuel, no smoke, and no tragic explosions such as plagued the upstart steamer men.

But in the end it was steam, more than the Civil War, the Suez, or the vulnerability of wooden hulls to fire, that killed the clippers. The two periods overlapped, and for a time there were combination craft, using both steam and sail. Then the day came when it was canvas that was the auxiliary, and then when the masts of merchant ships carried booms only for loading cargo. From the age of sail, risen to the glory of the clipper days, mariners moved on to the age of steam.

"Whoever commands the sea, commands the trade,
whoever commands the trade of the world commands
the riches of the world, and consequently the
world itself."

 —Sir Walter Raleigh

2

Robert Fulton and the

Coming of the Steamboat

STEAMBOAT: *a boat propelled by steam power.*

Convincing the maritime world of the worth of the clipper ship design was no easy matter as we have seen in the last chapter. Compared with this reticence on the part of the shipbuilding community, however, the resistance to the idea of using steam to propel a vessel was nearly insurmountable.

When Donald McKay was born, the steamboat was already about seventy-five years old. Not one man, but dozens in many countries had showed that sailors need not rely on the wind or muscle-power to move their craft from port to port. But sailors, whose dependence on sails gave them their names, fought with all they had against any shift from sail to the smelly, smoky, noisy, infernal machines spawned by a tea kettle! Robert Fulton's greatest achievement was not in operating a steamboat, but in successfully shoving the *Clermont* down the unwilling throats of the people in 1807, three years before the birth of McKay.

· *History of the Steamboat*

Man invented the wheel for two uses at about the same time: the potter found that his wheel aided him to make better utensils, and the wagon-builder was in business. The wheel became synonymous with transportation on land thousands of years ago; the first records of its use for traveling the sea date back to about A.D. 370. In a treatise entitled *De Rebus Bellicus,* an unknown Roman writer describes Roman men-of-war powered by ox-powered paddlewheels!

It was inevitable that the efficacious wheel would come into the maritime picture before too long. The way this occurred was quite natural and logical, although at first thought it seems rather strange. The fixed waterwheel for operating a mill was an early invention, dating probably back to 1000 B.C. The *floating* mill came later. In this device millwheels were slung from barges anchored in midstream where there was a good flow of water.

After watermills had been in operation for some centuries, some curious apprentice noticed that if he stopped the free-spinning wheel the raft tended to drift downstream. If he rotated the wheel *against* the current, however, he could halt the drifting. And if he turned the mill-wheel fast enough he could move upstream against the current—and seemingly against nature itself!

Thus the Roman military writer could describe ships of war powered not by sail or the oars of slaves, but oxen. Horses were used, too, and so paddlewheel craft of several "horsepower" doubtless navigated the water in the dim history of navigation centuries ago. By the seventh century Chinese warships were propelled by paddlewheels driven by the muscles of a human crew.

In 1472 Roberto Valturio of the Italian seaport of Rimini published a book called *De re militari* which contained a drawing of a craft propelled by five pairs of paddlewheels driven by coupled crankshafts. The military seems to have fostered much work toward the paddlewheel craft. About 1500 that many-faceted genius Leonardo da Vinci suggested pedal-driven two-bladed paddlewheels to propel boats.

From then on there were many similar proposals, and even actual models constructed of such paddle craft. One of the most interesting suggestions of all, apparently first made in 1664, was a compromise that should have appealed even to sailors. This grand invention would mount a windmill *and* paddlewheels aboard a boat! Such a craft might have moved along at a fraction of the speed sail alone would have provided, and indicates an unfortunate mixture of courage and shortsightedness in the same individual.

Thomas Savery's steam engines started the industrial revolution by successfully pumping water out of the deep English mines so that they could be worked. In 1702 Savery said about his invention: "It may be very useful in ships, but I dare not meddle with that matter." Actually, Savery was suggesting that the steam engine might serve to pump water out of the hold of a ship. He and James Watt after him would have little faith in the wild notion of using steam for locomotion or navigation.

Thomas Newcomen improved on Savery's steam-pressure water pump by adding a piston and rotary motion. This improvement came in 1712, and by 1736 another Englishman with the appropriate nautical name of Jonathan Hulls patented a steam-driven tugboat that used a Newcomen engine. For a variety of reasons Hulls' ship never reached the practical stage. The steam engine was still a bulky, heavy, and very inefficient piece of equipment. Fuel consumption was high and boilers had an embarrassing tendency to explode. Worst of all, the response of men who controlled the purse strings, and that of the general public as well, was something like, "If God had intended for us to sail in steamships why would there be wind?"

It was almost forty years after Jonathan Hulls' patent that a steamboat really put on a good demonstration. At least its inventor, Monsieur J. C. Périer, thought it good. His craft was driven along the Seine River in 1775 by a sizable steam engine with an eight-inch cylinder, but it achieved a speed of only a few knots. Observers scoffed and suggested that Périer get a horse or a sail, or else convert the thing to a grist mill. In 1883 the Marquis Claude du Jouffroy d'Abbans steamed his paddlewheel craft *up* the Saône River near Lyons. This craft, the *Pyroscaphe*, or "Fireship," was no toy but had a displacement of 182 tons. Still, it traveled at a speed of only a few knots and most observers thought its engine still resembled some work of the devil. Public response was apathetic and there was no interest or backing from shipbuilding firms.

There were some Americans interested in steamboats, too. One was John Fitch, who had been clock-maker, foundry worker, silversmith, surveyor, and soldier. For some reason he gave up his work to devote himself to steamboats. His first design seems clever even today. Instead of a paddlewheel, his craft would be driven by an endless chain of "paddlefloats." In effect Fitch had invented a kind of sea-going tank with caterpillar treads. Understandably there were mechanical difficulties with this advanced propulsion method, and he switched to a design using twelve oars, still to be steamdriven. By 1796 John Fitch had evolved the screw propeller that would eventually rule the sea, and he built a small craft fitted with one.

Fitch's work met the same enthusiastic response accorded his fellow steamboat inventors in England and Europe—plenty of laughter and little encouragement. There was no financial support forthcoming and the resourceful Fitch put two of his abilities together to finance further steamboat work. He painted a fine map of the great northwest area of the United States, and engraved plates for printing it in quantity. By selling the maps he helped finance a steamboat which plied regularly up and down the river carrying passengers between Philadelphia and Trenton.

Fitch had put his heart and soul into his revolutionary craft and was confident his hard work and clever ideas would pay off. But still there was no great public interest. Canal boats were the style now, and horses pulled them easily up and down the stream. Who needed John Fitch and his crazy steamboats that smoked up the river? Desperately Fitch appealed to state governments for financial help, or at least for some encouragement. When aid did not come he packed up and went to France, hoping that people there might be more receptive to his revolutionary ideas. But the French who had scoffed at the *Pyroscaphe* scoffed also at the upstart foreigner whose craft looked even crazier than those of the Marquis d'Abbans. In the end, Fitch returned to America and in 1798 killed himself at the age of fifty-five in failure and despair, a sad commentary on the scientific vision of his country.

Fitch had spurned the old-fashioned idea of paddlewheels, and another American also turned to radically new means of propelling a craft. James Rumsey had been born the same year as Fitch, and in 1787 he sailed his own craft along the Potomac. It had no paddlewheels, no oars, and not even the marvelous screw propeller that Fitch had turned to. Rumsey's steamboat pumped water in from the bow and ejected it from the stern—probably the first practical human application of the principle of jet propulsion!

On January 9, 1785, Congressman James Madison wrote to Thomas Jefferson, then the American Minister to France, "J. Rumsey, by a memorial to the last session, represented that he had invented a mechanism by which a boat might be worked with little labor, at a rate between 25 and 40 miles a day, against a stream running at the rate of 10 miles an hour."

In 1787 Rumsey demonstrated this remarkable craft on the Potomac, and among the admirers was General George Washington. But America was too busy becoming a nation, it seemed. There was little interest in the jet craft that seventy-five years later would be copied to produce perhaps the safest kind of propulsion for a vessel. Disappointed, Rumsey went to England and in 1793 a steamboat using his propulsion principle was successfully tested on the Thames. It was sizable, with a displacement of 101 tons. But James Rumsey tragically died of apoplexy before fame could come.

By now even Scottish inventors were interested in steam engines. Patrick Miller was one such shipbuilder who was convinced that sail was not the final answer. He built a paddle-wheel craft that attained a speed of several knots, with a power plant rated at 30-*manpower*. Unfortunately, his men could not maintain their cranking for very long and Miller wisely turned to steam power. In 1788 he successfully demonstrated his first steamboat on Dalswinton Lake in Scotland. Among the pleased passengers was the poet Robert Burns.

There were still powerful deterrents to the advancement of the steamboat, however. In 1803, the highly respected Philosophical Society of Philadelphia, whose members (including Benjamin Franklin) were familiar with the work of Fitch, Rumsey, and other steamboat pioneers, handed down a pronouncement about steam navigation. It was, the august scientists said, impossible! Furthermore, they listed six reasons why it was impossible. Fortunately, Robert Fulton did not believe them.

• Robert Fulton

Robert Fulton was born in 1765 in Lancaster, Pennsylvania. This was before there was a United States of America, and as a youngster Robert heard the fierce drumbeats of independence. He lived through the birth struggles of the country and, like Donald McKay, he knew the misery of a farm that broke his father financially and forced his return to the city and a tailor's job. The elder Fulton died early, and young Robert went to the city to make his fortune.

Unlike McKay, however, he had not set his sights on ship-building as his great goal. True, as a boy he and a friend named Christopher Gumpf played on the elder Gumpf's flat-bottomed boat and Bob Fulton mounted a pair of hand-cranked paddlewheels on it. He was mechanically inclined and inventive, too, but he wanted to be an artist. His father had among his friends the great painter, Benjamin West, and West encouraged Robert in his try for a career. In Philadelphia Robert Fulton found work painting jewelry for a shop, but worked so hard at supporting himself, his mother, and sisters that he fell ill. Recuperating in a resort in Bath, West Virginia, he was so encouraged by guests who saw his paintings that on returning to Philadelphia he opened his own studio.

Not far from his front door was the Delaware River, where John Fitch and James Rumsey were plying back and forth in their strange steam-powered craft. But Fulton was a painter, and his next move was to sail for England where he might study under the now internationally famous Benjamin West.

By the time he was thirty years old Robert Fulton was painting the portraits of nobility, exhibiting his work in the galleries of the Royal Academy, and in general doing quite well for an aspiring artist. But real fame was slow in coming, and maybe Fulton was beginning to suspect that while he was a good painter, he might probably never be a great one. Or maybe he was really an inventor at heart. At any rate, he began to spend less time at his easel and more at a drafting board he set up in his studio.

Back home he had invented—or re-invented—a paddle-wheel boat. In England canal boats were popular and it was this type of navigation that attracted the young inventor-engineer. He patented device after device bearing on canal transportation and also invented a marble-cutting saw and a rope-twisting machine. He even wrote a book about canal boats and then one day Fulton decided he would invent the submarine and a torpedo to arm the craft with. Actually, both of these had already been invented. In 1620, the year the *Mayflower* sailed to the new world, one Cornelius Drebbel had constructed an oar-powered undersea craft that worked. David Bushnell built one in America that in 1776 tried to blow up a British ship with an underwater torpedo. But for all the impression these pioneers had made, Fulton would in effect be inventing the submarine anew.

The style in those days was for inventors to go to France. Just why is not clear, for French inventors were not doing well either. Nevertheless, in 1797 Fulton went to France and built the submarine *Nautilus*. Here was a name to become famous in fiction and real life, and one day a *Nautilus* powered by nuclear energy would thrill the world. Fulton's wooden *Nautilus* was less fortunate. In 1800 he, with two sailors he somehow persuaded to go along as motive power for his strange craft, set out to destroy a British sailing man-of-war. The French had decided that if Fulton could do this, he might have something. Unfortunately, the tide was against him, and the inventor was probably lucky to return alive. The French finally made token payments for development of better submarines, but in the end Fulton was discouraged and gave up the idea of aid from Napoleon.

Help came instead from Robert Livingston, American Ambassador to France in 1801. Livingston, something of an inventor himself, had acquired the navigation rights for steamboats in the state of New York, but, unfortunately, he had no steamboat to make these rights worth anything. He had heard of Fulton, and thought perhaps that inventor could build just what was needed. Fulton was delighted with Livingston's suggestion, but first he wanted to go to England and try to exploit his submarine idea. If the French were not interested, maybe their traditional enemies the British might be. The British, however, were as shortsighted as their foes across the Channel. They did manage to delay Fulton's move back to America with promises and more promises, and also with the threat of denying him permission to take home a British steam engine for powering the steamboat he was to build for Livingston. But at long last the wrangling was finished and in the fall of 1806 Robert Fulton sailed for America. He had built an experimental steamboat in France and sailed it up and down the Seine at a disappointing speed of about three knots. He was confident he could do better with the next one.

In France, Fulton's troubles with his first steamboat had included having it sink at the dock during a heavy storm. Luck was better at Charles Brown's shipyard at Corlear's Hook on the East River in New York. But there was still

trouble enough. The big steam engine Fulton had purchased from Boulton and Watt had arrived, carried across
the sea in the hold of a sailing ship, of course. Now as the
monstrosity was unpacked, shipyard workmen gawked
and wondered what sort of madman was bossing this job.
A sailing vessel was a proved quantity; they could build
such ships almost with their eyes closed. But how did you
shape a craft to carry several tons of machinery, including
fireboxes and boilers that might explode and burn at any
minute?

As the freakish 150-foot hull took shape the frowns
turned to jeers. Only 13 feet wide, the craft, which Fulton
had named the *North River Steamboat*, resembled a top-
heavy water snake. The citizens coined a new name for it, a
name they felt it deserved. *Fulton's Folly* was the butt of
rude jokes of the day. Worse yet, a passing sailing ship ran
into the *Folly* "accidentally," for fun. Most sailors who
came to look at the new steamboat were surly.

Fulton was forced to hire guards to protect his craft and
the dock it was moored to. The work was harder, and took
longer than had been expected. Livingston was petitioning
the state of New York to extend the time period of his
navigation rights, and fretting about the clause that demanded a speed of four knots for the craft. Suppose the
jibers were right, and *Fulton's Folly* failed to deliver her
promise? She was Livingston's folly, too, and he had no
more money he could invest. The partners sought desperately for backing, but as Fulton himself put it, "Never did
a single word of encouragement cross my path."

By cutting all the corners he could and stalling his credi-
tors, Fulton managed to finish his steamboat. On August

9, four years to the day from the demonstration of his first steamboat in France, a nervous Robert Fulton fired up the furnace of *The North River Steamboat of Clermont*, as she was now called in deference to Livingston's estate on the Hudson. And miracle of miracles, the teakettle boat actually steamed a mile down the river and back! Delighted, but still tense, Fulton tied her up, doubled the guard, and busied himself for the next week with last-minute details and improvements that suggested themselves on the trial run. A turn around the river was by no means success. He and Livingston must steam up-river all the way to Albany and return. And they must average four knots while under way.

To make matters worse, a crowd of friends had been invited to take the journey, since this would be added proof of the practicality of the craft. Her name had now been changed again to simply *Clermont*, but even some of the passengers muttered to themselves that *Folly* still fitted her better. At worst she would explode and kill them all. At best she would sink and they would have to swim for their lives. But Livingston, with his career as a steamship tycoon at stake, had twisted the arms of family and friends and insisted they go along. For his part, Fulton sincerely wished that he and he alone could make the run north—a run that would spell either the reaching of a goal he had sought for years, or the failure of his second career.

With steam up, the noisy engine was put into motion. The *Clermont* moved away from the dock, and cries of pleased surprise drowned out the angry muttering. Then the engine quit suddenly and the male passengers began to curse their luck. Wishing he could slip over the side and disappear, Fulton, instead, had to face his disgruntled passengers and beg their patience for a few moments. If he could not find what was wrong, he told them, the trip would be postponed so as not to spoil their whole day. Then he ducked below decks and conferred with his engineer. Fortunately, the trouble was minor, and in a few minutes the engine was again pumping her pistons up and down and the big paddlewheels dripped Hudson River water as they shoved her out into midstream. The rest is history. In thirty-two hours of steaming the *Clermont* covered 150 miles against the wind and current, a speed of nearly five knots instead of the required four. Fulton and Livingston had made good on the navigation monopoly the latter held, and the way was open to exploit that franchise. For a bonus, Robert Fulton announced his engagement to Harriet Livingston, niece of his partner.

At age forty-two, Fulton had succeeded where no man had done so before. He had a practical steamboat, with an engine that would chug away by the hour and deliver many horsepower to her proudly churning paddles. Such paddles would push steamboats up and down rivers including the Mississippi, and soon they would travel along the coast and then out across the ocean itself. The death knell of the sailing ship was sounding in the hollow boom of a Boulton and Watt steam engine.

All was not smooth sailing for Fulton and Livingston, to be sure. Other men, including a relative of Livingston, challenged their navigation monopoly up and down the Hudson, and Fulton began to spend as much time in court as he did building boats. But in the long run, and for everyone, such competition was to the good. The steamboat was too big for one man to handle.

Fulton would build the warship *Demologos* for the U. S. Navy and experiment with a submarine named the *Mute* for its silent engine, but his death came tragically early to end his contribution to steam-powered craft. In 1815 he died of pneumonia. Now other men must carry on.

Other Americans would advance the river steamboat to coastal navigation. But the next great breakthrough, the iron ocean liner driven by screw propellers, would be the work of an Englishman, as his country belatedly realized the worth of the steamship and raced to catch the upstart Americans.

"That packet of assorted miseries which we call a Ship."

—Rudyard Kipling,
The First Sailor

3

Isambard Kingdom Brunel and His Great Ocean Liner

LINER: *a vessel belonging to a regular line; as, a trans-atlantic liner.*

We have seen that even Robert Fulton's *Clermont* in 1807 was by no means a pioneering effort in the field of steam navigation. Thirty-eight years before the first clipper slid down the ways in New York Harbor, the steamship that would eventually drive sail from the sea was no novelty. Why then did it take more than half a century from the time of the *Clermont's* chugging journey up and down the Hudson to establish steam on the world's sea lanes? There were a number of reasons, rather than a single cause, but perhaps the greatest single factor against the steamship was human nature. Man is a stubborn creature and he fights most change as he would a plague. One day men would also taunt Henry Ford with cries of "Get a horse!" and ridicule the Wright brothers to the extent that they had to travel to Europe and England seeking the recognition they deserved for their airplane. Even though most people in those lands demonstrated little interest in new ideas in shipbuilding, it was in England that the revolution began that carried steam from its modest chores up and down rivers, and safe coastal routes.

Among the men who contributed to the conquest of the oceans by steam one name has been lost in the more than a century since the phenomenal shipbuilding feats associated with it. And that is a shame for in itself it is a name to conjure with: Isambard Kingdom Brunel, the man who pioneered the giant ocean liners that led to the *Queen Mary* and other such leviathans of the deep.

None of the liner builders started from scratch, of course. From the point reached by Robert Fulton, other men began other great struggles toward the mastering of the sea by steam.

In the flush of elation and excitement following the successful voyage of the *Clermont*, Fulton's partner and backer could probably be forgiven for making the ridiculous statement that steamboats would one day cross the Atlantic! "Come now, Mr. Livingston," the diehards taunted. "We will admit your little craft has some applications as a riverboat, but do not get delusions of grandeur. Ocean voyages indeed!"

Twelve years later, the first transatlantic "steamship" sailed from Savannah, Georgia to Liverpool, England. One day another *Savannah*, powered with nuclear energy,

would make a similar pioneering voyage. In 1819 the proponents of steam hailed this passage as a great milestone,
which it surely was. But sailing men laughed in their beards.
The *Savannah* was a sailing ship with a steam engine
mounted amidships where its single smokestack stuck up
like a sore thumb. Her paddlewheels were collapsible, and
could be hauled aboard when not in use. "For use in sight
of land!" claimed the scoffers. "But as soon as she's out of
sight there's the end to the teakettle!" As a matter of fact
the *Savannah's* steam engine was used for only a total of
eighty hours on the ocean voyage that took several weeks.
One good reason the engine did not operate longer was
that it had used up all its fuel!

River steamboats were never far from shore and a pile of
firewood. If there was none cut, her engineers became
woodsmen and felled trees nearby. But on the great ocean
there were no such fuel depots. So sea captains laughed at
the smoky teakettles as sailing ships went around the world
with no fuel needed except that which the good Lord provided—the wind.

The success, or lack of it, of the *Savannah* bears out this
philosophy. She began her career auspiciously enough with
the honor of President Monroe's presence aboard for a
short cruise. Word of the forthcoming momentous sea
voyage made the English newspapers, of course, and the
Times of London announced that "A new steam vessel
called the *Savannah* packet of 300 tons burden, has been
built in New York for the express purpose of carrying
passengers across the Atlantic." But when the *Savannah* had
successfully used steam for part of her trip, and put into
port at Liverpool after twenty-seven days and fifteen

hours what happened? The sad truth is that nothing at all happened.

In the first place, there were no passengers aboard the plucky steamship. Perhaps none would risk their lives aboard a craft they feared might blow them sky high at any moment. Discouraged by the failure of England's people to even notice them, *Savannah's* crew sailed off to Denmark, Sweden, and finally Russia. The Tsar said some nice things about the steam craft when he inspected it, but that was about the only pleasant event that marked an otherwise completely useless trip. After visiting Norway, the *Savannah* sailed back to America. This time she didn't bother to fire up the steam engine and ship her paddle-wheels. If no one even noticed, why go to all that trouble?

Back home her embarrassed owners ordered the paddles and engine permanently removed. The holes were patched up, paint covered the telltale smudges of smoke, and *Savannah* became an honest sailing ship. In November, 1821 she was wrecked on Long Island, and that was the inglorious end of the first steamship to sail across the Atlantic. It was not a particularly encouraging beginning, and did nothing to make other bold entrepreneurs attempt to popularize steam. It remained for the Dutch to sail the Atlantic next with a steamboat, perhaps because they had heard nothing of *Savannah's* miserable failure.

By now the British were plying back and forth across the English Channel and even down the coast of Europe in perky little wooden steamboats. The Dutch bought one of these and renamed it *Curaçao* for one of their island possessions. They had the fantastic notion that it could sail from Rotterdam to Surinam in South America, a voyage much farther than the Savannah-Liverpool crossing. In 1826, when nearly everyone had forgotten the *Savannah*, the *Curaçao* departed Rotterdam with a load of mail and some passengers. One month later she landed safely in Surinam. Later she made a similarly successful return trip. Again, however, the feat did little but make sailing men laugh. With the coming of war against the Belgians, *Curaçao* was turned over to the Dutch Navy and there were no more ocean voyages for her.

· *Steam Versus Sail*

As late as 1830, steam ocean liners were still regarded as a ludicrous dream. But now at last the time was right, the stage was set. In 1831 the steamer *Royal William* was launched at Montreal. Built at Three Rivers, Quebec, fitted with English-built steam engines, the new ship was an ugly, squat tub. A 450-ton craft, she might make four knots in good weather. The windjammers roared with laughter, and turned away from this smoky blot on the horizon.

After seeing the *Royal William* steam ruggedly along on its haul between Quebec and the town of Pictou, however, shipper Samuel Cunard of Nova Scotia went home and wrote in his diary, "Steam-driven ships properly built and manned, can be established on the North Atlantic trade routes within measurable time, and could start and arrive with the punctuality of railway trains."

For years it had seemed that nothing could break the iron grip American shipbuilders had on the Atlantic run.

The fast sailing packets built in New York and Boston shipyards outraced the best of the British fleet. Speed and dependability were the lifeblood of this new kind of navigation. Gone were the days when leisurely voyages were the privilege of the East India Company monopoly. Now there was growing competition, and speed meant success.

The worst thing about the wild boasting of Yankee maritime superiority was that all of it was true! British shipyards simply could not build sailing ships to match those of the upstart revolutionaries. But suppose a steamship were used. A steamship not dependent on the vagaries of wind and weather, but running on a schedule almost as dependable as a steam locomotive!

Over in Liverpool there was a scientific authority named Dr. Dionysius Lardner who recited the cold facts and figures to prove that steam was a dream. A voyage from Liverpool to New York using steam all the way? "One might as well talk of making such a voyage from here to the moon!" Lardner cried to his delighted audiences. But despite Lardner and others of his kind, steam's time was approaching.

On August 18, 1833, more than a quarter of a century after Fulton steamed *Clermont* triumphantly up the Hudson, fourteen years from the time of the *Savannah's* voyage, the first continuously operating steam engine drove a ship across the Atlantic. *Royal William*, purchased by Samuel Cunard and others, carried a load of coal, a box of stuffed birds, a set of household furniture, six spars, one box, one trunk, an Irish harp, and—miracle of miracles—seven paying passengers. She vanished over the eastern horizon carrying the lives of her passengers and crew, and the hopes of Cunard's new venture. On September 11, *Royal William* anchored off Gravesend, her trip a complete success. The crossing took only twenty-three days.

Royal William, like *Savannah* before her, carried a full set of sail and used it to help propel her across. But the engines had operated for every one of the twenty-three days, and not just eighty hours as on the *Savannah*. Steam navigation across the Atlantic was no trip to the moon as Dr. Lardner continued to insist.

Sailing ships had proved they could deliver the goods, but no steamboat had yet matched the speed of sailing packets across the Atlantic. For another five years Cunard would continue to patiently plan his steamship line, trying time after time to secure the money it would take. One big problem was that steamboats cost more to build than sailing ships. And they cost money in fuel to drive across the sea.

Meanwhile, across the Atlantic, two British groups boldly pushed on with their own plans. In 1838, five years after the *Royal William* had steamed and sailed across with a handful of passengers and a token load of freight, another craft built for coastal service was likewise pressed into service for ocean navigation. Designed for the run from London to Cork, the *Sirius* was a three-masted topsail schooner, fitted with an "auxiliary" steam engine rated at six hundred horsepower. She steamed west on April 4, brazenly advertising her sailing, and promising boldly to return from New York on May 1. She was bigger than *Royal William*, but not much, and few who watched her sail out of Liverpool expected to see her return.

Somehow the owners had talked forty persons into actually paying a fare for passage. Miraculously they all reached New York eighteen days, and ten hours later, a new "record" for steamship crossings. She left Liverpool with 453 tons of coal and forty-two barrels of resin as fuel, and according to exaggerated newspaper accounts she made port in America only by burning up much of the furniture aboard, plus even a child's doll! Actually, there was coal left in her bunkers, although only a scanty fifteen tons.

Hot on *Sirius's* heels came what was the first ship ever built for steam power and the Atlantic run. The *Great Western* was nearly twice the tonnage of *Sirius,* and her steam engines produced 750 horsepower. She was the product of Isambard Kingdom Brunel, the "Little Giant" who had built England's railroads, and who now brashly asked why not extend the Great Western Railway clear across the sea to New York!

· *Isambard Kingdom Brunel*

Samuel Cunard was not an engineer. He simply decided what sort of ship was needed, and had it built. Everyone has heard of the great Cunard liners; few know anything about Isambard Kingdom Brunel, he of the strange name and the driving genius that would lead to the giant ocean liners of eighty thousand tons.

In 1793 a French engineer named Marc Isambard Brunel fled from home for his life. He voyaged in a sailing vessel to America, and made a name for himself as an engineer in New York. By 1799 he decided to return to

England. Within the year he had a job in a shipyard, and had married his sweetheart Sophia.

Among the projects Marc Isambard tackled was the making of new machinery for producing "blocks," the pulleys used in the rigging of sailing ships. In 1806, a boy was born to Sophia, after two daughters, and this youngster was named Isambard Kingdom. Ironically, he would make the block a relic of the past with his revolutionary steamships. But first he would engineer more conventional things with his father.

Bridges and tunnels are conventional, but the Brunels, elder and younger, did unconventional things with both. By 1825 they had tunneled successfully under the Thames, despite the fact that young Isambard himself was nearly drowned in a mishap in the tunnel during a cave-in. His father eventually received credit for his engineering genius and was knighted Sir Marc Isambard.

Young Isambard distinguished himself by building the Clifton Suspension Bridge at Bristol and the Hungerford Bridge spanning the Thames. He turned then to railroad building for the Great Western Railway, and for the next eighteen years he would lay almost sixty miles of track a year. However, he resolved to do something with ships, also, and he introduced the idea with characteristic vigor. The directors of the Great Western Railway were meeting to discuss the upcoming line from London to Bristol. Some of them were fearful of the great length of this track to be laid, but Isambard arose and differed with them.

"Why not *really* make it a long line," he said with a smile. "When we reach Bristol with the railroad, why not carry on to the west from there all the way to New York? We would call it the *Great Western*."

The reaction to this absurd suggestion was laughter, for hadn't Brunel been joking? Years earlier his father had been asked to consult on a scheme for steamships to sail from England to the West Indies, and the great engineer declined. "As my opinion is that steam cannot do for distant navigation, I cannot take part in any such scheme," he said. Strange talk for a man who himself had sailed on some of the first British steamers, and even made improvements to their engines. But his philosophy was that of the Americans who saw *Fulton's Folly* good only for river navigation, with wood for the furnace never far away.

Young Isambard had more vision than his noted father. When the learned pessimist, Dr. Lardner, lectured on the foolishness of ocean steamers, Brunel was one of the few to rise and furiously do battle. In October of 1835 he first proposed his "railway to New York," and in July, 1836, the keel was laid for the *Great Western*.

Once Brunel had thrown down the gauntlet to the marine world, there were other groups interested in the idea of steam navigation across the ocean. The British and American Steam Navigation Company of London, and the Transatlantic Steamship Company of Liverpool each ordered a ship of about the size and power of *Great Western*.

In July, 1837, *Great Western* slid down the ways in Bristol Harbor, far ahead of the competition. As work proceeded on her fitting out, the rival firms switched to smaller ships that could be ready sooner, the *Sirius* and *Royal William*, named perhaps for the earlier *Royal Wil-*

liam that had been sent from Halifax across the Atlantic by Cunard in 1833.

By March 28, *Sirius* was ready and departed for New York. It was the thirty-first of March before the *Great Western* was ready, and when she departed Brunel was on board. He was three days behind *Sirius* at the start, but still felt that *Great Western* could make up the gap with her greater power and better design. Then, two hours from the dock, tragedy struck, and for the second time in his short career, one of Brunel's creations almost killed him. As the ship sailed off the town of Leigh, smoke and flame suddenly shot from the engine room!

The engineer rushed to the boilers to save them from exploding, and the captain fought the flames with a hose. Suddenly the captain was knocked down by a falling object—Brunel himself, falling from a collapsing ladder as he hurried to help. Knocked unconscious, Brunel lay motionless in the water of the boiler room floor. The captain yelled for a rope to be lowered from the deck, and held Brunel's head above water until he could be hauled to safety. Meantime, the first mate had driven the burning ship up onto the beach.

At last the fire, caused by burning caulking around the boilers, had been put out, and it was found that aside from the slight damage from flames, the ship was all right. In great pain, but insisting that whatever happened to him the *Great Western* must sail and accomplish her mission, Brunel was taken ashore and put in a hospital. That evening the rising tide lifted the gallant ship from the beach, her paddlewheels churned, and she steamed out in pursuit of *Sirius*, ahead by five days. Even the staunchest enthusiasts in Bristol conceded that there wasn't a hope of beating *Sirius*, and the fire had dissuaded all but seven of the original fifty passengers.

Sirius thrilled New York when she steamed in after a nineteen-day voyage. It was a daring feat for the small craft, never intended for ocean travel. She had won the "race," for *Great Western* did not arrive until the following day. But when the thunderous cries had died down, wise heads knew that *Great Western* had achieved the real victory: Her crossing had taken only fifteen days, four days better than *Sirius*, and was far safer. For instance, there were still two hundred tons of coal remaining, and her large size made her steadier in high seas. Yet there was another accident of freak nature as *Great Western* celebrated her victory over time and the sea. The chief engineer, who had courageously saved the boilers by his quick action in England during the earlier fire, was scalded to death as he worked on the engines in New York.

Great Western loaded sixty-eight passengers and returned in great triumph to England, making the voyage again in fifteen days. Meanwhile, *Royal William* had crossed to New York in a little over eighteen days. In England Dr. Lardner was sputtering incoherently at the news that not just one, but several steamships had sailed the Atlantic. In America, newspapers wondered in print not whether steam could cross the Atlantic, but whether the added cost might not still rule in favor of sailing ships.

The British government was keenly interested in mail contracts, and Samuel Cunard boldly bid for the job at $275,000 a year. For this his firm would guarantee two voyages each month from Liverpool to Halifax and Boston, and return, with sailings on a strict schedule.

On the heels of the formation of Cunard's steamship line came loud cries from America. Her packet lines had been dealt a mortal blow; worse yet, her pride was hurt. In Congress a senator summed it up this way: "That type of protection [against British domination of the sea lanes] means only one thing—speed! Speed against which these British can never hope to compete. Speed of a magnitude such as the Government of Britain and its chosen instrument, this man Cunard, never visualized or could ever hope to achieve against America!"

The outcome of this indignant protest against Cunard was the formation of the Dramatic Line, under Edward Knight Collins of New York. Soon four 2,750-ton steamships were being built, giants nearly three times the size of Cunard's liners, and with 800-horsepower engines. Early in 1849 the *Atlantic* slid down the ways.

A sailing packet in those days cost in the neighborhood of $50,000, a sizable sum of money. When word got around that *Atlantic* had cost not $50,000, or $100,000, but the fantastic figure of $675,000, there were Americans who were sure their quest for speed had bereft those responsible for the Dramatic Line of all their senses. Close to three-quarters of a million dollars for a single steamship, when that amount would buy a dozen or more sailing ships! Here was folly to make Robert Fulton seem conservative.

To make matters even worse, hardheaded businessmen could show a deficit of thousands of dollars per trip in the operation of a steamship as compared with a sailing packet. Not only did the steamship spend money for fuel, it also had less cargo space available to pay for that use of fuel! Yet there was more to the matter than that, as men with clear vision could see. Steam's advantages would more than outweigh its high cost.

On her maiden voyage *Atlantic* crossed to England in ten days, sixteen hours to win the "Blue Riband" for speed, and the battle was on; a battle that would persist into our own times, with the blue ribbon changing hands many times. And it was "that man Cunard" who started the whole thing.

The reaction in England was just the reverse of the cheering in America over *Atlantic's* feat. A widely read magazine published a verse that put into words the feelings of many Britishers:

> "A steamer of the Collins Line,
> A Yankee Doodle notion,
> Has quickest cut the mighty brine
> Across the Western Ocean;
>
> British agents, no way slow
> Her merits to discover,
> Suggest we buy her just to tow
> The Cunard packets over!"

This verse was sung to the tune of *Yankee Doodle*, of course, and its effect was immediate. The British government ordered Cunard to speed up his crossings. He did so with a new fleet even larger and more powerful than the Dramatic Line ships. The *Arabia* and *Persia* averaged twelve knots, and brought the Blue Riband back to England with crossings of just a bit over nine days.

The coming of steam to the Transatlantic run was not all glory for the owners. There were tragic shipwrecks, too, and hundreds of persons perished. As early as 1841 the *President* disappeared with 136 passengers aboard. In 1854, as a third steamship line established by William Inman began to compete with Cunard and Collins, more sinkings marred the record books. Inman's *City of Glasgow* disappeared with 480 aboard. His *City of Philadelphia* was wrecked off Cape Race. Collins's *Arctic* was rammed in fog by the French ship *Vesta*, and sank with the loss of nearly 300 lives, including Collins's wife and children.

All the while Brunel's *Great Western* sailed on and on to ever greater victories. She was first to wear the prized Blue Riband, and she made sixty-seven crossings in eight years. During this time Brunel built bigger and more advanced ships. In 1838 he began designing the 3,300-ton iron-hulled *Great Britain,* then the largest iron ship in existence. As if this were not enough novelty, Brunel also adopted the screw propeller instead of the conventional paddlewheels to drive *Great Britain.* His engines boasted a precedent-making 1500-horsepower.

It was not until 1843 that the *Great Britain* was launched, and it was 1845 before she would sail for New York on her maiden voyage. On her first round trip she averaged fifteen days per crossing. With improvements she lowered this to thirteen days in 1846. Then in September of that year a freak accident in navigation drove the gal-

lant iron craft high and dry on the rocks near Dundrum
Bay in Ireland, miles from where her captain thought
himself to be! A faulty chart was blamed, but this did little
for the poor *Great Britain*, or the finances of Brunel's company, which had looked so bright. On this ill-fated voyage
the ship had been carrying 180 paying passengers, the largest complement for a steamer up to that time. Getting her
off the rocks at Dundrum put the Great Western Steamship
Company out of business. *Great Western* and *Great Britain*
were sold to pay debts.

Great Western was put on the Southampton to West Indies run and performed like clockwork for ten years.
Great Britain was fitted with smaller engines and re-rigged.
In 1852 she began the run from Liverpool to Melbourne,
Australia, carrying 630 passengers and cargo. In the next
twenty-three years she would make thirty-two such voyages. After that she served several different owners, and
was finally retired as a steamer in 1886. Even then she continued to be useful, as a "warehouse" for wool. She served
in this capacity until 1933, and her apparently indestructible hull can still be seen in the Falkland Islands today.
Brunel had produced the first practical steamer for ocean
travel; he produced also the first iron ship with propeller
drive. Perhaps most important, his structural designs resulted in the strongest craft yet built.

Brunel had failed to exploit his ideas financially, perhaps
because his concern was not mainly financial. While building the *Great Western* and the *Great Britain*, Brunel was
also still deeply involved in the building of railroads. He had
battles there involving his "broad-gauge" track and the
"narrow-gauge" of the opposition. Brunel was concerned

about the future of the railroad business, and by 1847 he was seriously considering retirement.

He was forty-one, and in his short life he had done more than most men in twice that time. He had married and had three growing children. Now he decided it was time to build his family a fine new house. For a number of years he devoted himself to this project, but by 1852 the lure of the ocean had possessed him again. He was dreaming and beginning to design a ship that would make the *Great Britain* seem a child's bathtub toy! His notebooks began to contain jottings like this: "East India Steamship. Say 600 feet × 65 ft × 30 ft." Here at work again was the amazing mind that had suggested the railway clear to New York.

No one but Brunel could take himself seriously at first. He talked of ships of twenty thousand tons, of fuel loads of seven thousand tons for a one-way voyage to Australia, or fifteen thousand tons in case it was necessary to take enough for the return. (Coal was scarce in Australia.)

Why such a monster, when *Great Britain* was proving herself so practical at only a fraction the weight? Brunel had a theory about the size of ships. It was based on cubes and squares, whereby the water resistance of a ship did not increase as rapidly as would its cargo-carrying capacity. If Ship A of five thousand tons cost $X per ton carried, Ship B of ten thousand tons would cost something less than $X per ton.

In 1851 the Australian Mail Company had retained Brunel as consultant for ships they wished to build for the Australia run. He advised making them five thousand to six thousand tons, and after the company recovered from the shock they went ahead and built the *Victoria* and the *Adelaide* to these proportions, although Brunel did not actually design them. Out of this contact came Brunel's eventual association with the Eastern Steam Navigation Company, and by 1854 they were building a "great ship" to cost about $1,000,000.

The *Leviathan*, as Brunel had appropriately named her, was to be 680 feet long, weigh 22,500 tons, and be powered by paddlewheel engines developing 3400 horsepower, and screw propeller developing 4900 horsepower! He said she would achieve a speed of fifteen knots or better, and be able to steam twenty-five thousand miles, or clear around the world, without refueling. This giant would carry five hundred first class passengers, and five thousand tons of cargo.

Like the *Great Britain*, *Leviathan* would incorporate the longitudinal "tube" design Brunel had used in his famous bridges. The hull would be so strong as to be nearly indestructible. But there were difficulties in her construction for a number of reasons. First, she was a vessel long before her time. Six times the tonnage of anything else afloat, and with a double bottom of "cellular" construction never before attempted, she taxed the ingenuity of her designer and also of her builder, Scott Russell. Personalities entered the picture, too, as well as apparent poor money-handling by Russell. With schedules lagging, and *Leviathan* not being constructed as intended, the company was forced to take her out of Russell's hands and complete her themselves.

Launching the *Great Eastern*, as she was called by the time she was ready for the water, was a tremendous project. She was to be slid into the river sideways, because of her great length, and many problems arose. Hard-pressed for money, the company had sold tickets to the launching, and thousands of spectators milled about. In the confusion, an onlooker was killed, and Brunel called off the launch.

Many weeks later, and after the expenditure of an additional £100,000 for the launch alone, the *Great Eastern* was finally afloat. With financial problems, Brunel was forced to eliminate some of the features he had intended. An interesting one was a gyro-stabilized platform for the navigator to use in taking his sights of sun or other heavenly body! This advanced concept was indicative of Brunel's genius.

He also had planned to light his ship with electricity, and to mount her compasses high on a mast so that the magnetic field of the hull would not give false readings, as had probably happened on the ill-fated *Great Britain*. To get the compass reading down where the navigator could see it, Brunel designed a clever system in which light beams were projected from the compass down to the deck!

With *Great Eastern* nearing completion, her designer's health was breaking. Plagued by nephritis Brunel journeyed to Switzerland for a rest. While there he tried to work on plans for the Greater Bengal Railway he had in mind, but his heart was with his giant ship.

It was 1859 before *Great Eastern* could sail, and by then Brunel was seriously ill. Although his death was imminent, he continued to drive himself and all those connected with the great ship. One of the experts who had been on hand for the launching had told Brunel cruelly what most of his colleagues must have really thought of the *Great Eastern* as a business venture.

"Turn her into a show," he advised. "She will never pay as a ship. She would make a substantial pier and her deck a splendid promenade; her hold would make magnificent saltwater baths and her 'tween decks a superb hotel, with an elegant restaurant, smoking, and dancing saloons, and I know not what else. I do not know any other trade at present in which she will pay so well."

Naturally, Brunel was stung by these frank words, and perhaps he feared their truth. The great Thames tunnel he and his father had built was not truly appreciated for decades after its completion. His two fine ships for the Great Western Steamship Company had not made any money, although for reasons certainly not Brunel's fault. But they would seem good investments compared with the nightmare career ahead of the *Great Eastern*. While Brunel lay in bed, waiting word of a successful shakedown voyage, his great ship sustained a terrific explosion he could hear in the hospital: An engineer had bypassed a safety device and blown up a boiler! Six men died of horrible burns. Shortly after learning what had happened, Isambard Brunel died, too. He was fifty-two years old.

Almost $4 million had been spent on the *Great Eastern*, and the original company had gone bankrupt. A new group persevered after the tragedy and actually steamed the ship several times across the Atlantic—a giant vessel with palatial accommodations heralding the great luxury liners that would be built decades later. With only handfuls of passengers and token cargo she lost money every trip, and sustained freakish damages that added to the trouble. After one crossing her captain retired because of a nervous break-down. Her backers were in about the same state, and at last the *Great Eastern* was sold at auction for the ridiculous price of $125,000.

Now she was put to the best use of her pathetic career, as a cable-laying ship for Cyrus K. Field's great venture. Because of her excellent maneuverability—by virtue of her paddlewheels *and* propeller, she could be turned in her own length or held steady in a single spot quite easily without the use of tugs. She laid telegraph cable from England to America, and from France to America. Then she went around the world laying other cables.

One of the men who stuck by her and was aboard when the Atlantic cable was at last complete told the story that long years ago, while *Great Eastern* was still being built, Field had visited her. Brunel said, "There is your cable-laying ship." Years later, as the venture with Field started, those aboard were stunned to encounter the tug *Brunel*—the name was a coincidence and no connection with the famous family—a kind of harbinger of good fortune. It was as though Isambard himself was there with them.

Great Western had been built for the Atlantic trade. *Great Eastern* was never intended for so short a haul, designed as she was for the Australia run. While there might still have been a place for her in that service, none had the vision to put her to the test. Soon the Suez Canal, that had sealed the doom of the clipper ships, wiped out all such hopes. With the shorter passage, smaller ships with less fuel could make the voyage. *Great Eastern* was far too large to squeeze through the Canal, and too large for just about everything except cable-laying. On one such project she sailed from England with a gross weight of more than thirty thousand tons.

After all the cables had been laid, evil days fell on *Great Eastern*. Brunel had been advised to turn the ship into a "show" and now that horrible thing happened. In 1886 she was anchored in the Mersey River, turned into a "floating palace, concert hall, and gymnasium." One writer described bands playing and acrobats flying through the air —a sight, he said, to break the heart of Brunel could he have seen it.

In 1888 the merciful end came for the great iron ship. She was sold at auction as scrap iron, for a price reportedly of $80,000. Even in this sad death, she gave birth to two legends, neither of them true, most likely. The first is that the wrecker's iron ball on a cable was invented to break her up, since Brunel had designed her with such tremendous strength. Second, it was said that the skeleton of a riveter and his helper were found sealed in a tomblike section of her hollow bottom. Here, the superstitious claimed, was the reason for all her troubles. She was a ghost ship, a floating jinx haunted by the spirits of the two who died so horribly in her innards!

Like her builder, *Great Eastern* died early. But like him, too, she pointed the way to the coming age of giant liners. In time other men would build ships as large and larger, and make money on them. Brunel made no money on his pioneering ships, but he made them first. That was his great contribution.

· Rulers of the Sea

Strong winds still blew about the oceans of the world, but by 1875 there were the winds of change. Sailing men could blame their defeat on the Civil War, depressions, the "dirty ditch" at Suez, or any of the other factors. But their ultimate nemesis was steam, in the form of floating teakettles transformed by men like Fulton and Brunel into the liners that ply the seas today. In their turn, these ships had to yield to newer methods of propulsion, and perhaps even newer means of crossing the sea.

"The strength of the ship is the Service,
And the strength of the Service, the ship."
—Ronald Arthur Hopwood,
The Laws of the Navy

4

John Ericsson

and the Modern Warship

MONITOR: *a heavily armored warship having a low free-board and one or more revolving turrets.*

When we think of our Navy today we picture large and fast high-powered ships of steel. These men-of-war mount huge gun turrets that swivel to hurl heavy shells for many miles. And the "sailors" aboard such craft know little if anything about handling sails. We may be tempted to think this was always so, because the picture of a sailing warship is hard to conjure up unless we have just seen a movie of such bygone days. Yet the days of "wooden ships and iron men" ended less than a century ago.

At one time, wind was the deciding factor in naval engagements. Cannon were fired broadside from the gun-ports of a ship of the line, and only in elevation could they be adjusted. Actual aiming of such old guns was done by swinging the whole ship. The notion of using a steam engine as power for a fighting ship was so strange that when the steam warship was finally introduced, operating procedures called for banking the fires and hoisting sail when in actual combat, lest sparks ignite the powder supply!

The ship as a weapon of war must date soon after the invention of the ship itself. From that distant past until the middle of the nineteenth century, changes in design had been mainly matters of degree. Ships were still built of wood and driven by sails full of wind. Such armament as they mounted consisted of cannon similar to those used on land, and their primary defense lay in speed and maneuverability. But in the nineteenth century there occurred several distinct revolutions in the fighting ship. These were the introduction of steam power, the screw propeller, armor plating, and more effective guns. A single man was a leader in each of these fields.

These developments had been suggested, or at least hinted, centuries earlier. But it was not until the 1800's that they could be put to use. This lag resulted from economic reasons, slow progress on the technological front, political considerations, and to a very large extent, human nature.

Along with those iron men who gave seafaring the great heritage it enjoys were men with heads of material at least that hard, and eyes that shortsightedly could not penetrate the fog of tradition they surrounded themselves with.

· Navies of the Past

The haughty protests of Admiralty men that "iron won't float!" were the more ridiculous in light of history. For example, King Hieron of Syracuse plated his ships with lead, using bronze rivets to hold the heavy metal to the ship's wood planking. How recently was this innovation tried? In the third century before Christ.

Another forerunner of true armor plating was the clever device of Norse seafarers in lining the sides of their craft with shields. Da Vinci suggested making ships bombproof by means of strong superstructures. In 1574 the Dutch *Ark of Delft* combined two new ideas: shotproof bulwarks and paddlewheels. The wheels were not steam-driven, but cranked by the ship's crew; however, the use of mechanical power rather than wind was of great importance.

When Japan invaded Korea in 1592, Korea's Admiral Yi-sun invented a "tortoise-boat" to fight back against the Japanese navy. This tough little boat was iron-plated, fitted with a metal ram, and very maneuverable. It succeeded in wreaking havoc on an enemy who was not prepared for such an untraditional opponent.

About a hundred years before the last wooden man-of-war went out of commission the first iron boat was successfully operated in the English Midlands. It was the product of builder John Wilkinson and was named *Trial*. This was in 1787.

America, by reason of her ticklish position with respect to Mother England, did much to advance radically new warships. In 1814 an inventor named Uriah Brown demon-

strated a craft fit for a revolutionary nation. This was a
steamer with shot-proof hull and a weapon for shooting
Greek fire, a pioneer "flame-thrower."

Even this advanced craft was no match for one named
Demologos, also launched in 1814. This ironclad warship
was designed by Robert Fulton, to add to his versatile out-
put of submarines and steamboats. *Demologos* was a tribute
to her inventor, who died tragically early, and before she
could be launched. But it did little for the U. S. Navy except set a precedent. Finished after the War of 1812, *Demologos* had nothing to do, and the Navy apparently could
see no point in experimenting with her against the day she
was needed. So *Demologos* ignominiously finished out her
days as a receiving ship at the Brooklyn Navy Yard. To
add injury to insult, she was blown up in 1829, either by
accident or—some say—by a disgruntled sailor. At any
rate, *Demologos* ended with the sad record of twenty-five
Americans killed and another nineteen injured in the blast.

Except for a few rare exceptions, then, the fighting
navies of the first half of the nineteenth century looked
much like those of the eighteenth and even of the seven-
teenth century. It is not correct to say that any one man
produced the modern warship, any more than it is correct
that one man invented the airplane, the radio, or the space-
ship. But in the nineteenth century there was one man who
seems to have done more than any other, and far more
than most, to bridge the gap from ships that Nelson made
famous at Trafalgar to those that would fight in World
Wars I and II. That man was John Ericsson. He was a
Swede but he moved early to England, and then to America, which country he never again left despite the treat-

ment he was often accorded by his adopted land. When he died in 1889 the maritime world was a far different place than the one he entered in 1803, and Ericsson had done much to make that so.

· *John Ericsson*

John Ericsson was born in a small village in Sweden, so far north it was almost within the Arctic Circle. His father was part owner and foreman of an iron mine, and young John learned about mechanical things early. When he was eleven years old the family moved to the site of a ship-canal project his father was to supervise. Here was John's first brush with destiny, although he could not know then that ships would command most of his great mechanical talents in the future. For now he concentrated on the science of canal building. By the time he was thirteen he was a salaried "leveler" or surveyor and had a crew of grown men assisting him in this important work!

When John Ericsson was sixteen his father died. His mother and sister had to take in boarders to support the family and, to help out, John joined the Army. Just as he had advanced rapidly on the canal-building project, young Ericsson soon became an outstanding soldier. He quickly mastered artillery drafting, and now he had the second leg toward the knowledge he would use later to make his great contribution to the shipbuilding world.

At the age of twenty-three, John had a captain's commission in the Swedish Army. He had continued his interest in mechanical things, however, and in his off-duty hours had built an engine. This was not a steam engine like those of the great James Watt in England, but a hot-air engine. So keen was Captain Ericsson on doing something with his new engine that he secured a discharge from the Army and sailed for England, taking along the little model that worked so well on wood fuel in Sweden.

Unfortunately, the coal used for fuel in England gave much more heat than wood. Ericsson's little hot-air engine warped so badly it was ruined, and his first chance to demonstrate his mechanical genius ended in embarrassing failure. Undaunted, Ericsson went into partnership with a Britisher and the two produced a variety of engines. They turned to steam engines but Ericsson did not slavishly copy the efforts of others. Instead he went on to invent important improvements like the "surface condenser" which was soon adopted by many engine builders.

By 1828 Ericsson demonstrated an engine run on compressed air supplied from some distance away through a hose. In 1829 he operated the first steam fire engine—forerunner of the fire engines used today all over the world. Here was an invention that would seem to have assured his fame and financial security, but such was not the case. Officials snorted and went back to hand-pumped fire engines! Suppose Ericsson's powerful stream of water injured someone, they demanded.

Ericsson also designed and built a locomotive in 1829. He did this from scratch in about seven weeks, when he belatedly heard of a competition for such a vehicle, with a prize of £500 for the winner. There were five locomotives entered in the contest but three were such poor designs they were eliminated almost immediately. Surviving were the *Rocket* of George Stephenson, and

Ericsson's *Novelty*. The *Rocket* was built in traditional British fashion, as heavy and solid as the Rock of Gibraltar. The *Novelty* was light, but well-balanced. It ran more smoothly than the *Rocket*, and flabbergasted everyone— including Ericsson and his partner—by traveling a mile in fifty-three seconds, the fastest speed any vehicle had yet attained. Ericsson was not to win the prize, however. Rules were changed during the trials to favor the sturdier *Rocket*, and *Novelty* had engine trouble. In the end the *Rocket* triumphed, but Ericsson had not done too badly for a twenty-six-year-old immigrant.

He persevered at his drawing board, and improved the designs of his hot-air engines which he claimed were more efficient that the steam engines of the day. He invented a sounding device for ships and perhaps his work on this idea swung him back on the course he was meant to take on the sea. In the ten-year period after the locomotive competition, Ericsson worked out no less than one hundred inventions. Thirty of these he patented, including a screw propeller for ships. Soon Ericsson was hard at work design-ing a ship especially for the screw he had invented.

These were exciting years of reward after his dismal earlier failures and it was now that John and his partner received the backing of Francis B. Ogden, the United States Consul at Liverpool, and in this contact there was another link with destiny.

In 1837 a tug named the *Francis B. Ogden* was launched on the Thames River. She was not so named for long. When spectators watched the *Ogden* tow a sailing ship at the speed of six knots they promptly dubbed her the *Flying Devil!* So great was the publicity attending this remarkable feat of a steamship with no conventional paddlewheels—in fact with no visible means of propulsion at all—that Ericsson succeeded in arranging a public demonstration of the *Flying Devil* towing a great Admiralty barge. Aboard the barge were officers of the British Navy, and they watched in consternation as the tiny forty-five-foot tug moved them through the water at the unheard of speed of ten knots!

Ericsson was jubilant. Against this convincing display of power how could the Admiralty refuse to adopt Ericsson's new principle of propulsion? They showed him exactly how a few days later. Back in 1816, when steam was making its smoky appearance, Admiralty men had decided that it was "their bounden duty to discourage to the utmost of their ability the use of steam vessels, as they consider the introduction of steam calculated to strike a fatal blow at the naval supremacy of the Empire." This was a frighteningly accurate prediction, of course. The introduction of steam by other powers would surely be a fatal blow to the British Navy, but the experts chose to bury their heads in the waves and discourage away with a will.

From Admiral Sir Francis Beaufort, famous for his Beaufort scale of wind velocities—as befitted a sailing man!—came a note to Ericsson. It contained the amazing pronouncement that the Admiralty had been disappointed in the trials! Perhaps there was more honesty here than met the eye, but it did Ericsson little good to know that he had been scuttled by a bunch of hide-bound old salts determined to keep sail supreme. Sir William Symonds, one of this group, remarked that even if the propeller had the power of propelling a vessel, it would be impossible to steer the craft!

To drive the knife deeper into Ericsson, a month later the Lords of the Admiralty commissioned Francis Pettit Smith, a British farmer-become-inventor, to build his propeller-powered craft, a design far less efficient than Ericsson's. In the ensuing financial difficulties, John Ericsson suffered the supreme indignity for a genius. He was put in the debtors' prison on Fleet Street.

Chafing in prison, Ericsson pondered the unfair fate that could pay for great ideas in this fashion. Finally, through the Act for the Relief of Foreign Debtors, he was released from prison and permitted to try to build a new life for himself.

His bankrupt partner had gone into a different business, and the best Ericsson could do for the time was a job as designer for the Eastern County Railway. He would not long serve in this capacity, however, for his steamboat *Flying Devil* had attracted the attention of another American than the Ogden she was built and originally named for. Robert Stockton had been in and out of the U. S. Navy, and in 1837 he was back in. Visiting England he met and was impressed by the Swede John Ericsson, and particularly by the tug, *Flying Devil*. Here, thought sailor Stockton, was the beginnings of a real steam-powered Navy for the United States he was so fiercely proud of. Upshot of the meeting was that Ericsson was commissioned to build the iron ship *Robert F. Stockton*.

Steam-powered, she would cross the Atlantic to be used in America as a canal boat. But Ericsson proposed much more than a lumbering canal boat to Stockton. He wanted to test a new naval gun on the *Stockton;* an amazing gun able to fire accurately despite the pitch and roll of the craft.

He also had many other ideas for modernizing the fighting ship; ideas that appealed to patriotic Americans. For his part, Stockton proposed that they build a steam warship to be called the *Princeton*, in honor of that city in Stockton's home state of Delaware.

Although Ericsson might have been too cautious by now to accept what was happening for a true indication of his future, he was at last started in the direction he would pursue for the rest of his life. He would become an American. And he would be one day hailed as "the man who saved the United States Navy." In England the *Archimedes*, built by Ericsson's rival, Smith, was already gathering barnacles from disuse. The great Lord Napier continued to proclaim that brave as British sailors were, "they did not go to sea prepared to be boiled alive." There seemed to be no hope for steam power in the Royal Navy. Maybe in America the picture would be different.

Captain Robert Stockton came back to England to inspect his namesake. He pronounced her fit, and she bore out this approval in her successful Atlantic crossing. Jubilant, Stockton returned to America and began to prod Washington in the direction of steam-powered fighting ships after the decades that had lapsed since Fulton's *Demologos*. When Congress authorized two paddlewheel steamers as men of war, Stockton pressed the legislators to commission John Ericsson to build the modern warship the two men had dreamed of two years earlier. And John Ericsson, late in 1839, set out for America aboard the steamer *British Queen*.

The hectic, twenty-day journey aboard the paddlewheel wooden craft strengthened Ericsson's conviction that his screw propeller would soon supplant that means of propulsion. Fortunately, he did not have to wait while the minds of the American Navy were made up—minds only a bit quicker than the British. For while he waited for the word from Stockton to begin the *Princeton,* Ericsson designed and built two dozen steam-powered, propeller-driven tugs, barges and boats for operators on the rivers, the Great Lakes, and even the coastal run down to Havana, Cuba.

At last, in the middle of 1841, the Navy signaled full speed ahead on the *Princeton.* For his advanced steam warship Ericsson submitted a figure of only $75,000, and waived any compensation for use of his patents, except as the government saw fit to pay him. Two years later, the *Princeton* was launched. She was so far ahead of any other warship in existence that she was truly in a class alone. Here was a metal ship, steam-powered, and driven by twin propellers, turning in opposite directions on the same shaft. She burned anthracite, rather than the customary soft coal, and she used "forced draft" with centrifugal blowers rather than the usual natural draft. The *Princeton* was, to date, the greatest achievement of John Ericsson.

Captain Stockton was overjoyed with the *Princeton.* As a demonstration of its superiority, he staged a "race" with Isambard Brunel's steamer *Great Western,* sailing on a return voyage to England. In New York Harbor the *Princeton* easily sailed circles around the best of England's steamers, delighting Stockton at her helm. With no time for such gloating, Ericsson himself was at his drawing board happily working on other craft he had been commissioned to build for shippers. But even as the *Princeton* gloried in her success, tragedy was shaping itself to dim Ericsson's great achievement.

John Ericsson had installed his new gun and carriage—which he named *Oregon*, for the fight with England over that boundary—aboard the *Princeton*. But Stockton had an even larger gun built and installed. He called it *Peacemaker*, and it was to be an added warning to England not to provoke America too far in the border dispute.

Ericsson challenged the design of *Peacemaker*, and warned Stockton against adding it to the *Princeton's* armament. But Stockton was firm in his resolve. *Peacemaker* was built (by men not qualified to build a wheelbarrow, in Ericsson's opinion) and mounted. Then off went the *Princeton* to Washington to show herself and her backer proudly to the assembled great of the nation. Stockton had told Ericsson that he would pick him up from the dock at Wall Street, but instead, the great warship steamed past without slowing, much less sending a small boat ashore! Somehow, Stockton had convinced himself that he was the *Princeton's* creator; perhaps he did not want Ericsson on hand to remind him, and Washington, otherwise.

On February 28, 1844, five hundred guests boarded the mighty *Princeton*, from President John Tyler downward. Even aging Dolly Madison was there. Beautiful women, elegant food, and music from the Navy band made the affair a festive one. Cruising down the Potomac, the great guns of the ship were unlimbered and fired. Toasts were drunk to one and all assembled, including of course the loquacious Stockton.

There it might have ended, a great triumph for Stockton, had not the Secretary of War decided he wanted to see and hear *Peacemaker* fired once again. The presence of the British sloop *Vestal*, which had brought a British ambassador to Washington to negotiate over the 54-40-or-fight controversy, may have had something to do with this request. Obediently Stockton had his gun crew load in fifty pounds of powder and ready the 225-pound shell that *Peacemaker* could hurl for two miles. He gave the signal —and *Peacemaker* erupted in one of the greatest tragedies in our naval history.

Instead of firing as intended, *Peacemaker* blew her breech to bits, much as Ericsson warned could happen. In the horrible shambles about the exploded gun men lay dead and dying. Miraculously, the President was unhurt. So, too, was the Secretary of War who had decided at the last minute to put some distance between himself and the gun. But the Secretary of State and the Secretary of Navy were killed instantly. So were three other high officials, and President Tyler's longtime personal servant. Seventeen sailors were seriously injured and Captain Stockton himself was hospitalized. From his bed he laid the blame—not on his own shoulders where it really belonged, but on those of his "assistant, an ingenious mechanic named Ericsson."

Ericsson could thank the tortured Stockton with perhaps saving Ericsson's life. But that was the only debt he owed the Navy man. Understandably, Ericsson refused to accept the unfair blame saddled on him by Stockton. A board of inquiry exonerated him, but this official judgment did nothing to erase the terrible effects of the tragedy on the *Princeton* and her future. Never would he receive any compensation from the Navy for his services for building the ship that the *Proceedings of the Naval Institute* would in 1879 admit had ushered in the age of iron.

After the tragic explosion aboard the *Princeton*, the controversy with England was peacefully settled with a boundary established not at 54° 40′, but on the forty-ninth parallel. *Peacemaker* was well named, although not in quite the way Stockton had intended. The damaged ship was repaired and Captain Stockton returned to command her. But most of official Washington turned against the new warship. In 1850, when Stockton resigned, undoubtedly a man broken in spirit, *Princeton*, too, was immediately broken up in the scrapyards. For almost twenty years there would be another lapse before ship design would move ahead from the point Ericsson brought it to in 1843 with the *Princeton*.

He was able to sell several revenue boats to the Treasury Department, and a few others to commercial interests and foreign governments. But the Navy wanted no part of Ericsson. He built hot-air engines at great development cost and even built a ship named the *Ericsson*, powered with such "caloric" engines. But the ship foundered in a storm and lost him and his backers a fortune. Pettit Smith, the Englishman who had also invented a screw propeller, sued Ericsson, as did others. Court battles took time and money, and there were periods when Ericsson was in the red with no prospects of success, except for his great mind.

In 1848 Ericsson became an American citizen. During this period he also met many visitors from abroad. Among the latter was a seventeen-year-old youngster named Alfred Nobel, seeking information for his father about the hot-air engines John Ericsson had experimented with even before he left his native Sweden. Nobel had not yet startled the world with his new explosive, dynamite.

Welcomed to many scientific societies, Ericsson was asked to prepare exhibits for England's famed Crystal Palace Exhibition in 1851, and he sent over seven of his inventions that impressed Queen Victoria among others. But his troubles continued despite all these tributes. At one point he told a friend he was actually on the verge of ruin, and that he must do something, anything, to buy bread for himself. He did. His caloric engines, adapted for commercial use, sold by the thousands for $250 apiece, and once again John Ericsson was solvent.

In 1854 he had conceived the idea for another warship, one to make even the *Princeton* seem old-fashioned. But the time was not yet right. He would wait until the War Between the States before he again dedicated himself to the nation that had yet to pay him a cent for his work on the *Princeton*.

The model Ericsson built in 1854 was of an armor-plated warship, equipped not with mere guncarriages such as he had installed on the *Princeton*, but a "turret" that rotated a full 360 degrees. The model gathered dust for seven years, and Ericsson called it his "hobby." But when the South seceded, Ericsson did more than simply align himself on the side of the North; he offered to build the new ironclad for President Lincoln, seeking "no private advantage or emolument of any kind."

The shortsightedness of the American Navy was now painfully evident. Fulton had built the *Demologos* in 1814. Ericsson had built the far superior *Princeton* in 1843. Yet in 1861 the North had no ironclad of any kind, and word came that the South had floated the scuttled warship *Merrimac*, rechristened her the *Virginia*, and was in the process of making her into a floating fortress that no shells could penetrate! A man was needed to save the U. S. Navy from its worst defeat, and fortunately that man was at hand. John Ericsson told authorities he could build his *Monitor* for the relatively low cost of $275,000. Far more important, he could launch her one hundred days from the time the word was given to start. The word came, and the shipyard swung into action.

It was seemingly an impossible task that Ericsson had volunteered to do. The *Merrimac* was already being rebuilt when the government considered Ericsson's proposal. Not a single actual working drawing existed for the *Monitor*. No such ship had ever been built, and most of the Navy experts did not believe it ever would. It would capsize, they protested. It would sink like a rock. The gun crews would be killed like rats in a can full of firecrackers. But Ericsson fought them off with one hand while he built the *Monitor* with the other. The contract was signed on October 4. On January 30 a weird craft that has since been called a cheesebox on a raft slid down the ways. Instead of sinking, the *Monitor* floated like a raft. Her hull was 172 feet long, and a fourth that much in beam. Atop the hull was a "tin can" of a turret mounting the great eleven-inch Dahlgren guns and carriages.

· *Meaning of the* Monitor

The *U.S.S. Monitor* was commissioned on February 25. But on February 24 another warship had been commissioned. She was the *C.S.S. Virginia*, the reborn *Merrimac* lost to the South when at the Hampton Roads shipyards. It would be a battle against time all the way. Between the *Merrimac* and the North stood only old wooden sailing ships. On the night of March 6, the tiny *Monitor*, untested and not even "shaken down," steamed south to meet the invader from the Confederacy. It was fortunate that Ericsson could not know until later that his newest ship would meet heavy seas in the North Atlantic and perhaps narrowly miss the fate of his unfortunate *Ericsson* some eight years earlier.

On March 8 the dire predictions about the invulnerability of the *Merrimac* came true. At Hampton Roads the dreaded ironclad rammed and sank the *Cumberland*. The *Minnesota* and other vessels were run aground, and the *Congress* surrendered in the uneven battle. There was nothing to prevent the same fate from befalling all of the Northern fleet except an untried tin can on a raft, churning its way toward the larger enemy.

On March 9 the *Monitor* reached the embattled ships and the five-hour battle that ensued is history. When it was over, the *Merrimac*, four times the size of the tiny raft with guns, and mounting ten guns to *Monitor's* two, limped off to lick her wounds.

Strangely, it was an earlier product of Ericsson's great genius that sparked the ironclad ship. The naval guns *Oregon* and the *Peacemaker* had stirred the Navy brass to ponder whether ships could withstand their fearful penetrating power demonstrated before the tragic accident. The South's *Merrimac* was one result. The *Monitor* was the other.

Nine months later the gallant *Monitor* sank accidentally in a storm at sea, but this was no reflection on Ericsson's design. A whole fleet of similar craft would maintain a tight blockade of the South for the rest of the war and hasten its end. John Ericsson, who had adopted America as his native land, was hailed as the greatest man alive, the man "who saved the United States Navy."

John Ericsson would go on inventing things from better ships to motors that actually ran on sunshine. He would donate thousands of dollars to charities in his beloved Sweden, and proudly receive an honorary degree from a university there. Never would he receive a penny from the American government for his own work, either on the *Princeton* or the *Monitor*, and when he died there was not even enough money in his estate to pay the modest bequests he made. He died owing the world, but not half what the world owed him.

"There is a silence where no sound may be,
In the cold grave—under the deep sea,"

—Thomas Hood,
Sonnet, Silence

5

John Holland
and the Submarine

SUBMARINE: *a warship designed for undersea operations.*

In the thousands of years since the first primitive seafarer
learned to navigate a stream men learned how to stay
above the surface of the water. They floated precariously
at first, with death by drowning waiting for the unwary,
and then so safely that most sailors never bothered to learn
to swim. Having thus mastered the art of staying afloat,
why did man perversely plunge beneath the sea? There
were many reasons, as there usually are for any new development, and prime among the reasons for the submarine
was man's inherent curiosity.

There is a fascination to the unknown. Columbus was

proof of this in 1492 when he sailed for the "edge" of the earth. He thought he knew what was out there, but he wasn't sure. Curiosity killed the cat, and many humans have gotten into water over their heads in this manner. Among them are those who went down *into* the sea in ships.

It is interesting to note that few of the inventors of new kinds of ships were sailors themselves. Robert Fulton was a painter. John Fitch was a surveyor and engraver. James Rumsey was not a nautical man and Isambard Brunel was a builder of bridges and railroads. Perhaps this is because such men are not conditioned by custom to accept things blindly. Experts of England's Royal Navy actually predicted that iron ships would not float. Sailing men ridiculed attempts with steam. These men knew it was foolish to try to improve on what was obviously the best way to get the job done. Most inventors did not have the advantage of this heritage, otherwise we might still be clinging to a log and kicking our way across the water.

In spite of all sorts of odds including ridicule, the horrible dangers beneath the sea, and the lack of money for experiments, submarine inventors did succeed in creating underwater craft that could master the treacherous domain beneath the waves. Today giant submarines, with a displacement thousands of times greater than early submersibles, and powered with atomic energy, sail around the world with no difficulty.

• *History of the Submarine*

As early as 400 B.C. man had begun the invasion of "inner space." Nearly two thousand years before Columbus found the New World, divers were plunging into the sea and accomplishing tasks ranging from cleaning ship bottoms to slyly cutting loose anchors, or even sawing holes in the bottom of enemy craft. Thus the sport of skin diving didn't begin in the 1940's with the invention of the aqualung, but centuries earlier.

A trained diver may stay down as long as two minutes, breathing oxygen his own lungs can hold. But two minutes didn't suffice for these pioneer frogmen. Forerunner of the diving suit was the diving "bell," named for its bell-shape. Long ago men of science knew that the pressure of air in an inverted vessel would hold out the water, and so brave men had themselves lowered into the deep in bells constructed of wood, and later of metal. Among such early divers was Alexander the Great, whose exploits at the bottom of the sea have been embellished by admiring scribes until we read that he encountered a gigantic whale while down for an exploring trip, and had to remain there three days until the curious mammal finally swam away. Actually, it would be many centuries before man succeeded in submerging alive for such a long period.

It was Leonardo da Vinci who in the sixteenth century wrote the first scientific treatises on underwater equipment. He invented the "Mae West" inflatable life preserver, and also a primitive snorkel device through which a diver could breathe as he swam submerged.

Da Vinci was a secretive scientist who did not believe in publishing his work. What he wrote in his notebooks was done in a kind of coded shorthand so that those without the proper security clearance did not have access to his amazing inventions. Even in his notes which were not published until years after his death, Leonardo did not disclose some of his undersea secrets. He had perfected, he claimed, a device with which a man might stay at a great depth for long periods of time. But the inventor feared that evil men might use such a powerful advantage for wrong purposes. For example, they might sink boats by undermining them from the bottom, a trick that he felt should not be used even in war. This strange philosophy would be reiterated centuries later by some of Napoleon's military advisers. Undersea warfare was just not honorable.

We will never know how Leonardo actually solved the problems of breathing at great depths and what his other underwater devices were. But by 1620 another inventor, less concerned about the wrong uses to which his ideas might be put, not only designed a submarine but actually built it and demonstrated it.

Cornelius Drebbel was a Dutch inventor living in London. The same year the *Mayflower* sailed to the New World with colonists fleeing England, Drebbel launched a strange-looking craft on the Thames River. It was large enough for a dozen oars to protrude from the sides but in other respects it resembled conventional rowboats not at all. Instead of being open, the top of the boat was covered with canvas, securely attached to the sides and sealed to make it waterproof. For the trial run, the inventor and a crew of rowers climbed down through a hatch in the top, and then closed the hatch after them.

Curious boatmen, and a few spectators on shore watched in amused curiosity. How in the world would the crazy Dutchman see where he was going? A few minutes later they decided it made little difference. The weird craft promptly sank beneath the waves! Would-be rescuers were alarmed and angry at a lunatic who would venture from shore in such a leaky boat. Then, before they could locate the sunken craft, it popped back to the surface some distance down the stream!

Here, three and a half centuries ago, was the first successful submarine. For that is what the strange craft of Drebbel's was. The men in the crew stroked the fixed oars and propelled the craft not only forward, but downward as well. In perfect safety the bold sailors aboard sailed not on top of the water, but as much as fifteen feet beneath it. A flickering candle furnished light, and so advanced was Drebbel's engineering, that he even included an air-conditioning system with "a chemical liquor which would speedily restore to the air such a portion of vital parts as to make it again fit."

It is reported that among the passengers Drebbel took with him beneath the Thames was none other than King James I, following in the watery footsteps of earlier ruler Alexander the Great. In all, Drebbel seems to have built three undersea craft, but there is no record that these submarines did any more than prove their ability for the intended purpose. However, a writer named John Wilkins echoed the thoughts of Da Vinci without having read his manuscripts. Wilkins said of Drebbel's craft:

"It may be of very great advantage against a navy of enemies who by this means may be undermined in the water and blown up."

The nautical world was not yet ready for Drebbel and his remarkable craft. Perhaps the colonization of America overshadowed the idea of submarines. Drebbel was able to do little with his invention, even with the advertising the King's voyage must have provided. Neither was any other submarine inventor successful for some 150 years. Then, in 1776, a college boy built a quite successful undersea craft.

David Bushnell was an undergraduate student at Yale when the Revolutionary War broke out. He wanted to do something to help the cause, but instead of donning a uniform to fight the redcoats he designed and built a submarine. Bushnell's sub was named the *Turtle*, for that is what it resembled, floating in a vertical position. It was made of wood and covered with leather. Inside was barely room for one man who had to be captain and crew. He must surely have been busy, for there were pedals and cranks for both hands and both feet. One propeller furnished horizontal motive power, another pulled the craft up or down. Steering was done by a rudder, and there was a buoyancy chamber in the bottom to which water could be admitted or expelled by a pump. Two more pumps afforded air conditioning, one pumping in fresh air through a primitive snorkel, while another forced out the stale air.

Panes of glass let the submariner look out from his tiny conning tower, but there was a built-in safety device that closed a hatch in case the glass was broken. Even this small feature of the *Turtle* represented an amazing engineering achievement. But of what worth would the weird craft be to the embattled Americans? It was a warship, Bushnell told amazed naval experts to whom he took his invention. Besides the submarine, Bushnell had built a torpedo, too, and devised a means of attaching it to enemy ships below the waterline.

In operation, the *Turtle* was to submerge out of range of British warships off shore and navigate unseen up under the craft. Then the busy submariner would attach the torpedo to the enemy hull by twisting a special screw device that would bore into the planking of the unsuspecting ship. With the explosive charge attached, the *Turtle* would back off, setting a timing mechanism on the torpedo to give sufficient time for a getaway. And that would be the end of the enemy ship.

The *Turtle* actually was tried out under battle conditions. Bushnell himself got sick and was unable to make the run, but a sergeant volunteered and was taught how to operate the craft. He actually maneuvered it under a British man-of-war but was unable to drill through the copper plating of the hull. Forced to leave the ship, he did jettison the torpedo which blew up near the Britisher and at least threw the enemy into momentary confusion.

The most famous name in submarines is *Nautilus*. Jules Verne immortalized this craft in his book, *Twenty Thousand Leagues Under the Sea*. Captain Nemo's submarine was a wondrous craft, with comfortable quarters, air conditioning, electric lights, and many other advanced features. But the fictional *Nautilus* was not created until 1869. The real *Nautilus* was navigating the English Channel off

France in 1800, twenty-eight years before Verne was born! And its designer and builder was Robert Fulton.

We have already discussed Fulton's trip from America to Europe, and then to France where he built *Nautilus* and demonstrated it for the French government. *Nautilus* set out on a mission like that of Bushnell's *Turtle*, but was not even that successful. With Fulton aboard as submarine skipper, and two luckless crewmen who cranked like mad to drive the early U-boat beneath the sea, *Nautilus* tried to sneak up on a British ship. But time and tide were against her, and she never did catch the Britisher. Later Fulton did blow up a surplus ship anchored off shore for test purposes, planting a torpedo on the hulk from *Nautilus*. But by then France and England were on better terms, and the French military powers thought such tactics were too sneaky. Nothing came of Fulton's first attempt at building a radical new type of boat, even when he tried it on the British and later the American Navy. He had to switch in midstream to the steamboat to win a place in history for himself and his inventions.

Another submarine called *Le Nautile* was built in 1809 by the Couessin Brothers in France. In 1846 a Frenchman named Payenne used a sub for underwater work on a breakwater in Cherbourg Harbor, the first use of the submarine for useful peaceful purposes. But no one seemed particularly interested, and Monsieur Payenne had no more success than Fulton had before him in those same waters.

An unusual submarine was built in 1855 by the German, William Bauer of Kronstadt. His *Le Diablo Marin* submerged during a demonstration for the court of Alexander II in Russia, and a band of four musicians serenaded the king from the lake bottom!

The Revolutionary War in 1776 had sparked the *Turtle*. In 1864 another war, this one the American Civil War, prompted the building of a craft known as the *Hundley*. Resembling the *Turtle*, but larger and manned by a crew of as many as nine, the *Hundley* succeeded in blowing up the *U.S.S. Housatonic* in Charleston Harbor. Unfortunately for this first successful fighting submarine, it, too, was so damaged in the explosion that it sank with all its crew alongside the stricken man-of-war.

For about 250 years after the first successful submarine, its motive power continued to consist of human rowers or crankers. Drebbel used a dozen oarsmen, but David Bushnell introduced the idea of the screw propeller. Here was an unusual occurrence. It would be near the middle of the next century before steamboats successfully adopted the screw instead of paddlewheels, yet Bushnell demonstrated its effectiveness in 1776. Fulton, too, used the hand-cranked propeller in his *Nautilus*. But although submarines pioneered the screw propeller, it was some time before mechanical power would supplant manpower beneath the sea.

There were very good reasons for not mounting engines in undersea boats, of course. The only engines available were steam driven, and these required great quantities of air to burn their wood or coal. Air was a precious commodity in a submarine; Fulton had found it necessary to snuff the tiny candles in his *Nautilus* from time to time to conserve the air supply for breathing.

In 1880 a clever English inventor named Garrett built a steam-powered submarine. This had an engine with a folding smokestack and a good-sized boiler. On the surface, steam pressure was built up with a roaring fire until the boiler was about ready to burst. Then the fire was put out, the smokestack lowered, and the watertight covers fastened. Garrett's sub dived and went on her merry underwater way as long as the steam lasted—a distance of only several miles. Then it surfaced and the process was repeated. Obviously, his was not the final answer to powered undersea craft.

Another steam submarine was built by an inventive Swede named Nordenfelt. In addition to steam power, Nordenfelt added torpedo tubes to his craft, following the tradition that an undersea craft must be designed as a fighting ship.

Clever as these solutions to a tough engineering problem were, the early steam submarine was doomed almost as soon as it was launched. Not only because of the shortcomings of the system, but more importantly because of the coming of a new power supply. The steam engine had prompted increasing interest in the dynamo, a device for converting mechanical energy into electricity. With the dynamo came other generators, electric motors, and even storage batteries. As with the steam engine, major effort in this direction came in England, and two Englishmen, named Campbell and Ash, built the first all-electric submarine.

The electric submarine was a tremendous advance in underwater navigation. Campbell and Ash produced a craft powered by two battery-powered electric motors developing about one hundred horsepower, and traveling about seven miles an hour submerged. It could remain underwater for eighty miles on one charge of the batteries. The electric motors produced no harmful exhaust that would endanger the crew and did not require a supply of air as did steam engines.

Gasoline engines were beginning to take over some of the jobs of steam by now. They were lighter and more powerful. But still there was the problem of the need for air supply for the engines, and the deadly exhaust they produced. Clever engineers combined gasoline engines and storage batteries. For running on the surface the submarine used its gas engine, which also charged the batteries with a generator. When submerged, the craft ran on its electric motors. Another advantage of electricity was quietness of operation, a feature of importance in a military operation.

Thus far, most of the work on submarines would seem to have been done in Europe. English, Swedish, and French inventors had produced and operated many submarines; even Fulton's craft was introduced in France. But in America interest was stirring, too, and in 1873 there came on the scene an Irish immigrant who would within a couple of decades become known as the father of the modern submarine. His name was John P. Holland.

· *John Holland, Father of the Modern Submarine*

The name Holland hardly sounds like that of a fighting Irishman and perhaps there is truth in the statement of one writer that it is merely a corruption of the original O'Houlihan. Whatever the true facts, the man who surely deserves the name of "father of the modern submarine" was born John Philip Holland. This was in the year 1841, in County Clare, Ireland. Young Holland was educated at the Christian Brothers School in Limerick, and upon completion of his studies he became a teacher himself.

From age eighteen until thirty-two, Holland was faithful to his calling, a mild-mannered, serious-faced young man with a rather bedraggled moustache and rimless eyeglasses. But beneath the seeming calm of his exterior there burned a heart fiercely dedicated to freedom for Ireland from England's grip. The tragedy of the potato famine was everywhere plain to see, and like other Irishmen, Holland blamed the British, whose rule he considered oppressive. There must be some way to strike a blow for freedom, and John Holland vowed to find that way.

In 1873 he at last rid himself of the shackles of British control. He left Ireland and crossed the Atlantic to America seeking employment as a teacher. Shortly after arriving in Boston, the port he first touched, Holland visited the library. Coming down the stairs, he fell and broke a leg. It was hardly an auspicious start, but perhaps it shaped the destiny of John Holland and the submarine as well.

In his continuing search for a weapon to be turned against the British, Holland had come onto the tiny submarines used by the South during the Civil War. Stories of the *Hundley* which had sunk the *Housatonic* fascinated him, and he read everything he could find concerning the fateful undersea craft. During his convalescence he began to make drawings of his own version of a one-man submarine, a sleek, cigar-shaped design driven by a pedal-operated propeller, and steered with vertical and horizontal planes controlled from inside.

Holland had everything now but the money, and that was the hard part of his scheme to come by. Meantime, he had traveled to Paterson, New Jersey, and was teaching school to support himself. He was still actively concerned with the Irish freedom movement, and in this way he was introduced to the revolutionary Fenian Brotherhood. These patriots in America had raised thousands of dollars to be used to overthrow the British in Ireland, and schoolteacher Holland convinced them that they should invest a sum of money in his submarine. By now his plans included a torpedo and the Fenians delightedly heard him tell how his craft would become the scourge of British ships.

With money at last, Holland got busy on actual construction of his craft. In 1874 George Brayton had invented a new kind of gasoline engine, and Holland incorporated that powerplant into his tiny submarine. Then he put the craft into the Passaic River and proceeded to cruise about beneath the surface. With it he proved that he could submerge and surface at will, but beyond that the gallant attempt was of no practical value, certainly not as a warship.

He had started work in 1877. By 1879 he had given up on the first submarine, and begun to build a much larger craft. This new design, financed again by the Fenians to the tune of some $13,000, would carry three men and a torpedo fired by compressed air. To build the undersea boat he commissioned the Delamater Machine Shop, located on the East River in New York.

Not surprisingly, the submarine required two years to complete. Holland, fussing and fretting over the complicated problems he had posed for himself, had left teaching and become a "crackpot inventor" laughed at even by the machinists and boat-builders working on his submarine. The newspapers poked fun at the strange craft, and named it the *Fenian Ram*, implying that it was to be used to butt against the British warships.

The *Fenian Ram* was remarkably successful. It cruised at better than five miles an hour submerged, and could remain below the surface quite a while. But Holland was far from satisfied with the *Ram* as a real fighting ship as yet. Eagerly he turned to the building of a third *Ram*, this one about half the size of the second. By now it was 1882, and the Fenian Brotherhood were becoming very impatient. They had invested $15,000 or more in the undersea craft, and thus far John Holland had given them nothing in return but promises of a practical craft soon. So one dark night the Brotherhood succeeded in stealing both the latest submarines and setting out with them for Long Island Sound!

Somewhere in the night, the newest of the Fenian war fleet foundered and sank in deep water, never to be recovered. The inept pirates reached New Haven, Connecticut, with the larger craft and demanded that John Holland come there and help them proceed with further tests, since he was the only man qualified to operate the *Ram*. By now Holland had invested almost ten years of his life in designing and building a weapon for Ireland; the ridiculous actions of the Fenians soured him completely, and he refused to go to New Haven. The *Ram* ended its days ignominiously stored away in a warehouse, and John Holland retired from the submarine business.

Before long, however, he tackled another prospective

customer for his submarines. Holland, disappointed and frustrated by the Irish patriots, went to Uncle Sam. In the mysterious ways of the military, the Navy sent the inventor to the Army to peddle his boat. Equally mysteriously, the Army bought it!

The torpedo tubes in his earlier craft had been too much for Holland, so he was satisfied to leave the armament of the Army sub to an "expert," one Lieutenant Zalinski. Zalinski was an inventor, too, and his specialty was heavy guns. The "Zalinski boat" that resulted when the two got their heads together was to be a submersible gun battery capable of sneaking up on a shore-based enemy and shelling it with no warning.

John Holland's luck ran true to form; the Zalinski boat was a complete failure. It cruised at about half the speed of the original *Fenian Ram*, and the only damage it ever did was to itself by colliding with an obstruction. Again Holland swore he was through with submarines. But by 1889 he was making another gallant try.

For reasons that surely did not include the Army's Zalinski boat, the Navy was now interested in submarines— it said. Feverishly Holland began the design of a new craft that would combine all the things he had learned on his previous boats. He entered the competition and was rewarded with victory. He had the best design, for all the good it did him or the Navy. The winds of favor blew another way now, and the submarine project was a casualty.

It is a miracle that when the Navy again announced a competition in 1895 there was among the eight contenders the name of John Holland. He was fifty-five years old now, and had spent more than half his life dreaming and sweating over and in his submarines. The old Fenian fire to chastise England had waned, but apparently his interest in submersible craft was something that no amount of discouragement could completely sink.

The toughest competitor was Simon Lake, but Holland again was pronounced the winner. This time, though, something else happened. The Navy awarded a contract, and the figure set was $150,000! A jubilant Holland formed the J. P. Holland Submarine Boat Company. To the Columbian Iron Works in Baltimore went the job of actual construction, and the chagrined Delamater Machine Shop must have wished it had treated the "crackpot" more kindly.

It was two years before the *Plunger* was completed. Its designer by now was a sick man, physically sick and sick at heart as well from the ridiculous changes forced on him by the Navy experts. The Army had compromised the Zalinski boat into a failure; now the Navy gave the *Plunger* the same treatment. A gleeful Simon Lake predicted his rival's craft would indeed live up to its name—it would plunge straight to the bottom and bury itself in the mud as a French *Plunger* had done before her. Holland was about ready to agree. For one thing, the Navy had insisted on cramming not one engine but three into the undersea craft. The 1500 horsepower generated so much heat that the crew could not tolerate it.

Long before the Navy refused to accept the *Plunger*, Holland knew she was a failure. A lesser man might have taken whatever profit he could have salvaged and gone back to schoolteaching, but Holland was a born submariner. On his own initiative, and with the backing of a

New York businessman, he designed a new craft and began to build it. It would be named the *Holland*, and at long last, America would have a submarine worthy of the name.

Even this final success was not without its horrible moments. A workman left a valve open, and the *Holland* sank at her dock. Only the genius of an electrical engineer—fittingly named Cable, by the way—saved the electrical wiring from sure destruction from rust. Cable simply hooked up electric power to the wires, enough of it to heat them and dry them in time. This same Cable was soon the skipper of the *Holland!* Another time, the men below decks began passing out and had to be rushed to the surface. A leaky exhaust pipe had nearly asphyxiated the lot of them, Holland included. After that he installed a cage of white mice in the engine room to detect carbon monoxide gas.

In the end the *Holland* was an unqualified success. She could make seven knots on the surface with her gasoline engines, and five while submerged and running on electric power. She could surface and re-submerge in a matter of seconds. For a price of $150,000 the Navy purchased the *Holland*, dubbing it the *SS-1*, the first of a long line of submarine craft. This was in 1900, and by now the Holland Company had become the Electric Boat Company, the firm which half a century later would produce the world's first atomic-powered craft.

The second of the Electric Boat submarines was named the *Fulton* in honor of America's earlier inventor. The Navy was still busy evaluating the *Holland*, and not ready to add to its sub fleet, so the *Fulton* was sold to Russia. Five others were sold to Japan but, ironically, there was little joy now for Holland. His business acumen did not match his skill as a designer of submarines, and he was gradually being shoved aside as head man in his own company. Bitterly he denounced the officials, and even the Navy personnel he dealt with. They would have nothing to do with him now, he said sadly.

Sickness and the pressure of building submarines had turned John Holland into a crotchety old man, a skinny, stoop-shouldered "crackpot" peering nearsightedly around his spectacles. There was more irony awaiting him. He died in August of 1914, just as World War I began, the war in which the submarine would at last accomplish what countless men since David Bushnell had predicted. Six weeks after John Holland died, a German U-boat sank not one, but three British cruisers. The ghost of the *Fenian Ram* seemed in evidence, but John Holland's submarines would soon go into action on the side of the British he had hated for so long.

· *The Bridge beneath the Sea*

Today our country and other major powers operate great fleets of giant subs. Submarines are said to be our strongest line of defense, and thus represent the most important present use of underseas craft. It is to be hoped that some happy day in the future the commercial possibilities of the submarine will be realized and bring about a change in the dictionary's definition of it as a military weapon.

Just before World War I, in which the submarine was used with such devastating effect, Germany sailed her merchant sub, *Deutschland*, across the Atlantic. The war put an end to this application of the undersea ship, but men like Simon Lake continued to work toward peaceful uses. Explorer Sir Hubert Wilkins was another advocate of such peaceful aims, but the ill-fated *Nautilus* he tried to navigate to the pole failed far short of its goal. Years later the atomic *Nautilus* would succeed and again arouse interest in this challenging navigation under the ice. Some day, perhaps, submarine freighters and tankers will ply the polar routes safely and economically.

A newspaper drawing of the clipper ship *Flying Cloud*. (COUR-
TESY OF CULVER PICTURES, INC.)

The first steamboat, Fulton's *Clermont*, on its way to Albany.
(COURTESY OF CULVER PICTURES, INC.)

The *Great Western* entering the port of New York after crossing the Atlantic. (COURTESY OF CULVER PICTURES, INC.)

The fight between the *Monitor* and the *Merrimac*. (COURTESY OF CULVER PICTURES, INC.)

The *U.S.S. Holland*, one of the pioneers in submarines. (COURTESY OF CULVER PICTURES, INC.)

The *U.S.S. Nautilus* entering New York Harbor. (COURTESY OF THE U.S. NAVY)

The *U.S.S. Nautilus* (COURTESY OF THE U.S. NAVY)

A British-made hovercraft being tested for use in warfare. (COURTESY OF THE U.S. NAVY)

The bathyscaph *Trieste* being loaded aboard the *U.S.S. Point Defiance* by a floating crane. (COURTESY OF THE U.S. NAVY)

"The catastrophe of the atomic bombs which shook men out of cities and businesses and economic relations, shook them also out of their old-established habits of thought, and out of the lightly held beliefs and prejudices that came down to them from the past."

—H. G. Wells,
The World Set Free

6

Admiral Rickover

and the Atom-Powered Ship

ATOMIC ENERGY: *energy that can be liberated by changes in the nucleus of an atom.*

With the invention of the sail, early mariners discovered the ultimate in economic sea transportation—fuel costs on a sailing ship were zero. It would be thousands of years before internally powered ships challenged the supremacy of sail, and even when such craft had demonstrated their effectiveness it would take almost a century for steam, and then other engines, to displace wind power on the world's oceans.

In time, steam won the sea battle. Then it, too, was replaced by gasoline and diesel engines that were cleaner, more powerful, and more efficient. But even as these newer engines were pushing steam into the background, events were taking place that were destined to put steam back in ships. The atomic age was not just an age of bombs and radioactive fallout, but an age that swept over the sea and under it as well. Long before the atom bomb first burst on a startled world, some scientists had predicted that the power of the atom could drive a giant passenger liner across the ocean on a thimbleful of fuel. Early steam engines were terribly inefficient, converting only a few per cent of the total energy in the fuel into power. But even if they could be made 100 per cent efficient, steam and other power methods would remain capable of extracting only the tiniest amount of the energy locked in the coal or oil or whatever they burned. Now, by wrenching the atom apart, man was able to convert some of its matter into energy, creating a "fuel" that was terribly powerful.

Destruction came first from the atom; constructive uses of the fearful amounts of power unleashed took longer. But there were men who persevered in spite of the handicaps and disadvantages so readily apparent in the new source of energy. By carefully controlling the atomic reactor, an explosion could be prevented. Instead, great quantities of heat were produced and heat, of course, could do useful work. For example, it could drive a steam engine!

Science writers dug up the old predictions of sailing a *Queen Mary* across the Atlantic on a thimbleful of fuel, and a great cry arose for such a power plant. Unfortunately, the task was not easy. Besides the danger of explosion was the continuous problem of radioactivity that could kill passengers and crew if not safely contained. There was also the problem of size. Atomic reactors were giant affairs that might take up all the available space aboard a ship. And the fuel they used, efficient though it was, was so expensive that driving a ship with it would cost far more than using conventional fuels. The whole idea, pessimists claimed, was a brave dream and nothing more.

One of the most convincing arguments was that of economics. There could be no denying that an atomic ship would cost more to build than a conventional craft. It would cost as much to fuel it, too, in spite of the fact that it would use only pounds of fuel as compared with the tons that diesel-powered ships used. So, even discounting the hazards present with atomic power, where lay the advantage? To be sure, the atom ship could sail at top speed without the penalty of greater fuel consumption faced by the diesel engine. But who needed that extra speed?

The problem was not simply to design the atomic ship. It would be built only by a man willing to fight courageously against the unequal odds facing him. And it would be a military craft, a submarine, that would break through the atomic barrier at sea.

· *H. G. Rickover, Atomic-Ship Pioneer*

Hyman George Rickover was born in Warsaw, Poland, on January 27, 1900. When he was four years old his father moved the Rickover family to Chicago. Mr. Rickover was a tailor, and he could provide the necessities of life for his children. In addition to George there were two daughters, however, and the family had little money left over when all the bills were paid. As a result George worked at odd jobs even while going to school.

In high school he went to work as a messenger boy for Western Union, pedaling about delivering telegrams from three o'clock in the afternoon until eleven at night. Because of this outside work, and the fact that he was slightly built and of a retiring nature, young Rickover could not participate in sports or social activities. Indeed, there was hardly time enough to get his studying done, and he found it necessary to attend summer school to make up for classes he failed. The only time young George Rickover made the news was at the Republican National Convention in 1916: he had his picture taken as he delivered a telegram to Warren G. Harding, then a senator from Ohio but destined to be elected President in 1920.

Perhaps this brief public exposure helped to get Rickover a Congressional appointment to the U. S. Naval Academy at Annapolis upon his graduation from high school. Knowing his prospects for college were slim without this sort of help, George jumped at the chance and immediately left for a preparatory school in Maryland. He paid tuition of $300, feeling he needed help in passing the strict entrance examinations for the Academy. Yet he soon decided that the prep course was doing him no good and he quit, forfeiting his hard-earned money! For the next two months he studied by himself, and then successfully passed the examinations and reported to the Academy—only to come down with diphtheria and be put in the infirmary for weeks.

Faced with another long session of "cramming" to catch up and keep up with his classmates, plus the handicaps of limited funds (he had only two dollars a month for spending money) and his own withdrawn nature, Rick, as he was now called, also endured endless hazing at the hands of up-perclassmen. No athlete, he failed in his tryouts for swimming and fencing. He was, his classmates wrote, "Neither a star on the gridiron nor a terror in the pool . . . He is a thorough Englishman in regard to humor . . ." Despite all this he finished in the upper quarter of his class, largely because of his scholarship.

In 1922 Rickover graduated from the Academy and decided to stay in the Navy. Much of military life he deplored: unnecessary regulations, unwritten laws, cocktail parties and other social life, waste, and inefficiency. Maybe he could do something about that; at any rate he was going to try. In the meantime here was a chance to travel and see the world, while getting a continuing education.

There was a delay in being assigned a post after graduation, and instead of relaxing, Rickover got himself a scholarship at the University of Chicago and studied psychology and history during the long summer while he waited for transportation to the West Coast. Finally, in the fall, he got passage on a transport, whose name was more prophetic than the young ensign could know. The ship was the *Argonne*.

He was assigned to the destroyer *La Vallette*, but spent some time on the *Percival* before reporting to his own ship. On the *Percival* he received a startling introduction to the hazards of Navy life when, temporarily in charge while the skipper visited his home, he heard an explosion and helped pull an injured sailor back aboard. The explosion was caused by a whiskey still the men had been operating below decks!

Aboard the *La Vallette* he was soon made Engineering

Officer and served well in that capacity for two years. Next he went to the battleship *Nevada*, where he became Electrical Officer. Rickover worked so hard modernizing her communications system that he once informed the captain he was too busy to have dinner with him.

After five years of duty Rickover was eligible for postgraduate work at the Naval Academy, and he eagerly took advantage of the opportunity. Returning there in 1927, he began studying for a master's degree in electrical engineering. As was the practice, he was sent to Columbia University in New York to pursue this goal.

With his electrical engineering degree behind him, Rick was now assigned to the *California* as Electrical Officer, the post he had so capably filled aboard the *Nevada*. He didn't want it. Instead, Rickover applied for submarine duty. He had been on battleships; now he wanted to learn something new. But the Navy told him he was too old. He was only twenty-nine, and it irked him to be classed as an antique. By chance he met his captain from the *Nevada*, Rickover told him his troubles, and the Captain, now an Admiral and an important Washington figure, recommended that Rickover apply for subs once more. He did, and this time he was assigned to the Submarine School at New London, Connecticut for three years duty. While at New London, Rickover married Ruth Masters, whom he had met during his electrical engineering studies at Columbia.

In 1931, he was assigned to the submarine *S-48* as Engineering Officer. The assignment promised to be anything but dull. Built long ago by Simon Lake, *S-48* had sunk on a test voyage, fortunately with no casualties. The sub's sister ships *S-50* and *S-51* had both sunk. *S-49* narrowly averted this fate when one of her batteries exploded while the sub was cruising at sea. The *S-48* had been lucky so far, but soon after Rickover came aboard she too was struck by the trouble that had plagued the others. Forty miles off Long Island, smoke was detected coming from the battery room. The startled submarine captain ordered his men on deck and closed the hatches to keep air from the suspected fire in the batteries. But Engineering Officer Rickover pulled on a gas mask and groped his way through the dark interior of the sub to the battery room. Pulling up the floorboards, he found the blazing battery and smothered the fire with blankets.

Later that year the young officer performed another courageous act when a sailor on the *S-48* fell overboard in the Panama Canal Zone. Rickover plunged in and saved the man from drowning.

From the *S-48*, Rickover went to Philadelphia for a land-based job as Inspector of Material. Here he made a name for himself as a thoroughgoing officer, although he did little to increase his popularity with those whose operations he questioned and changed. In 1934 he went back to sea as Engineering Officer of the *New Mexico*, and in 1937 he received his first command. It had been a disappointment to Rickover that in the sub service he had not reached the top, climbing only to second in command of his ship. Now that he was finally the Commanding Officer of a Navy vessel, there was little joy in it, for she was the *Finch*, a mine-layer in Asian waters, doing such degrading jobs as towing targets for other ships to shoot at. Besides this, the *Finch* was so rusted that it was possible to kick holes in her! But Rickover not only kept her afloat, he instigated a repair program, and even put everyone to work chipping away at rust spots and painting the ship with red lead.

Happily his stay aboard the *Finch* was short. Officers with fifteen years service could apply for "EDO" or Engineering Duty Only, and Rickover lost no time in doing so. This relieved him of command of the *Finch*, and he went to the Naval Station at Cavite, in the Philippine Islands, soon to be the scene of America's ignominious defeat by the Japanese.

Next he went to the Electrical Section of the Bureau of Ships back in Washington. Now a captain, with a proven ability to get things done, Rickover continued to work miracles of red-tape cutting. But he was stepping on many toes in the process, and was far from the most popular captain in the Navy.

Soon America was at war, and Rickover moved from one Navy installation to another in the States, performing miracles of expediting first one project and then another. Through his drive and efficiency, ships damaged by Japanese action were salvaged and quickly repaired. But Rickover didn't want to serve out the war years safely at home. He wanted an assignment in the Pacific, and in 1945 he got it, going to Okinawa to establish a fleet repair base to back up the invasion of the Japanese home islands. And after V-J Day, Rickover made a name for himself putting the fleet in "mothballs." At the same time, however, he was doing something far more important. He was laying the groundwork for bringing into being a new kind of ship— the atom-powered ship.

· *Birth of the Atom Sub*

As far back as 1939, a Navy scientist named Dr. Ross Gunn asked for an appropriation of $2,000 for research of the phenomenon of nuclear fission. A handful of scientists thought there were possibilities in the atom for ship propulsion. But in 1942 the Army took over all research with uranium; the Navy was ordered to support the Manhattan Project, and the building of a bomb which eventually ended the war in the Pacific and opened up the Atomic Age.

There was a clamor at the war's end for peaceful applications of atomic power, and one of the first attempts in this direction was initiated by the Monsanto Corporation, one of the contractors involved in atomic research. Monsanto invited representatives from the government to come to Oak Ridge, Tennessee to study the feasibility of such things as atom-powered aircraft and ships. Leader of the eight Navy men delegated to go to Oak Ridge was a captain who had proved his abilities in the past to get jobs done: Hyman G. Rickover.

Rickover listened with interest to General Electric engineers' talk about an atom-powered destroyer, operating on uranium fuel more than 2½ million times as powerful as coal. Another application impressed him even more. Dr. Philip Abelson had suggested building an atomic submarine. Here, Rickover felt, was the ideal test bed for atom power. Of all ships, the submarine most needed such power. Because the atomic engine needed no oxygen to support it, the Navy would have a craft capable of remaining submerged for long periods of time. Also, if an atomic pile could be built small enough to fit into a submarine, Rickover knew it could be done for almost any craft. Early in the game, then, he committed himself to fight for the atomic sub. The craft could have had no stauncher advocate, but the path would not be easy.

Rickover was no diplomat. "You will like him," someone said, "if you are a man of foresight and imagination. If not, you will hate him, and he will hate you." Unfortunately, not all those connected with the atomic ship program were men of foresight and imagination.

The first setback that Captain Rickover and his team received was the appointing by the Navy of another group, apparently duplicating their work, with its head superior to Rickover. Unknown to Rickover, the Navy had signed contracts with General Electric for more than $2 million for a "breeder reactor," rather than the simpler "naval reactor" that Rickover favored, allotting it only a tiny $30,000. Rickover wanted engineering to begin at once but the Navy officially favored more research.

To make matters worse, the Monsanto Project came to an end in the summer of 1947. The word was that Rickover and his assistants had about completed their usefulness in their nuclear posts for the Navy. For what looked like their last official act the men toured nuclear installations throughout the United States, meeting the top men in such work, including atom scientist Dr. Edward Teller, and expressing their conviction and enthusiasm for an atomic submarine. Meantime, in Washington, it was suggested that Rickover be given the post of "declassification officer" at Oak Ridge.

The Navy had stalled on Robert Fulton's warship and submarine; it had frustrated John Ericsson and his metal warship idea. Now with a new *Nautilus* in prospect the same kind of resistance was evident. Outside the Navy some scientists argued against building a military vessel to use atomic power. In Washington Rickover was downgraded to "special assistant for nuclear matters." His new office had earlier been a ladies' powder room!

It was time for Rickover to begin working the single-handed miracles that had marked his long years of service to the Navy; he got busy on the seemingly impossible job. There was still some money left on one of the projects that had originated at Oak Ridge. Rickover succeeded in talking the few scientists who remained into switching their work to a "naval reactor." What had been an industrial nuclear pile became overnight the Rickover naval pile.

To get more backing for his idea, Rickover conceived the idea of having Admiral Chester Nimitz of World War II fame sign a letter asking for a nuclear submarine for the Navy. It was a bold plan, and one that took much work. But just as Dr. Teller had gone to bat for Rickover earlier, now some Navy men saw the worth in Rickover's plan. Among them were Commander Beach, a submarine skipper who was a hero in World War II, and Admiral Mills, Chief of the Bureau of Ships. With their encouragement, Admiral Nimitz, who had once been a submariner himself, signed the important letter. It had taken two months to get this job done.

The letter Nimitz signed went to the Secretary of the Navy. In the post-war military world the Navy was scrambling to find itself, and the idea of an atomic sub was one that appealed. The Navy might thus gain some of the prestige enjoyed by the Army and the Air Force with the atomic bomb.

Next Rickover got busy prodding the Atomic Energy Commission; first with a letter which the Commission pigeonholed, and then with speeches before hundreds of scientists and military leaders. If the AEC would join with the Navy, Rickover said, an atomic submarine could be aiding the Navy by the mid-1950's. When this approach still failed to jar the AEC from its indifferent attitude, Rickover drafted another letter, stating that the Navy was prepared to develop the naval reactor alone if need be. Finally, the AEC realized that it must cooperate with the Navy, and in May of 1948 it agreed to sanction work on the naval pile at the new AEC Argonne National Laboratory in Chicago, Illinois. It had been the Navy transport *Argonne* that carried Rickover to his first Navy post way back in 1922. Now another Argonne was helping him realize his dream of the atomic sub. Just getting started had taken a precious nine months.

Since General Electric was busy at work on the experimental breeder reactor, Rickover convinced Westinghouse to tackle the naval pile, insisting that it be designed to use water as the heat exchange medium, instead of liquid metal as in the General Electric pile. With the work under way at last, Rickover next turned his attention to setting his administrative house in order.

The Nuclear Power Branch, duplicating the original task force Rickover headed, had all but put him out of business and was still serenely moving along. Rickover knew that there could be but one organization in charge of the atomic sub, and boldly he went to his boss, Admiral Mills of the Bureau of Ships, and asked him to choose. Mills chose Rickover, and another hurdle was passed.

There remained even harder jobs. Rickover had to arrange for millions of dollars in financing for his project. He had to inaugurate production of the rare metal zirconium so that it would be available in quantity and at prices far cheaper than the almost half-million dollars a pound it cost when he found need of it. An even more important job was convincing the men working on the *Nautilus* project that the finished submarine was only years away, instead of being some dream of the distant future.

"The *Nautilus* is 95 per cent engineering," he told them, "and only 5 per cent theoretical physics! We already know that $E=mc^2$. What we need is men to hammer a reactor together!" In 1949 he was telling them that the *Nautilus* would be completed in five years. His enthusiasm was contagious. Soon the scientists and engineers on the project were not only echoing his bold prediction but making it come true.

The most modern submarine reverted to steam for propulsion. Its atomic power plant simply produced great quantities of heat to drive the steam engine. But the heat was of a kind marine engineers had never used before, and required lead shielding to safeguard the crew. It also had to be designed for long service, so that expensive tear-downs wouldn't be needed. Westinghouse proposed to build a "land-based" power plant first, not worrying about size and weight. Then, having worked out the general idea of the atomic engine, the firm would build another one small enough to fit into the *Nautilus*. This was standard procedure and it made sense—to everyone but Rickover.

"No," he said. "The land-based design must fit *inside* the submarine hull." Rickover knew that if he could force the engineers to do this he would save valuable time. For example, General Electric was estimating eight to fourteen years' development time for its experimental breeder reactor!

Eventually Westinghouse compromised; they would contruct two reactors. One would be their originally planned land-based experimental model. Another, with a schedule only slightly behind the first, would fit inside the *Nautilus*. Now it was time to select a builder for the submarine itself.

Rickover had hoped that the Navy's own submarine yard at Portsmouth, New Hampshire, would build the craft. But he was told it was incapable of doing so, for various reasons including funds. The private Electric Boat Company works at Groton, Connecticut—where the pioneering Holland subs were built at the turn of the century —got the job. In 1950 work was in progress not only on the atomic power plants, but on the *Nautilus* hull itself.

Then Rickover worked another miracle. He convinced the AEC, and General Electric, that the latter should drop its long-term breeder reactor project and concentrate on the small naval reactor Rickover had advocated all along. General Electric went along with the idea, and now there were two power plants in process for the *Nautilus*.

Thus far the *Nautilus* was a well-kept military secret, but in 1950 the first of many articles describing the new craft was published. Immediately the cry went up for other atomic weapons, including an aircraft carrier, and even an airplane. Interest also grew in an atomic ship for the Merchant Marine.

Far out in the desert at Arco, Idaho, workmen were building the first submarine ever to be put together in the desert, hundreds of miles from the sea. In Groton, Connecticut, the Electric Boat Company was building a sub just as strange. It was made of wood, and called a mock-up. Ordinarily the mock-up and the actual metal craft were in the same shipyard, and only a few hundred feet apart. But with *Nautilus* the engineers and workers had the problem of 2500 miles of distance to complicate their job. There was another complication—no one had ever built a nuclear sub before. It was a challenge to all concerned.

In July of 1951, another kind of trouble threatened the *Nautilus* project. A Navy Selection Board "passed over" Rickover for promotion to Rear-Admiral. This came as a disappointment to Rick, but perhaps no great surprise. He had a history of being a nonconformist and apparently he had stepped on the toes of many on the Selection Board.

The Navy's first *Nautilus* had been purchased in 1913, and it was only one of many which shared that historic name. In June of 1952 the keel for a new *Nautilus* was laid at Groton. The ceremony was a gala affair. President Harry Truman was on hand, and so was the Governor of Connecticut, the Chairman of the AEC, the Secretaries of Army, Navy, and Air Force, plus a host of other dignitaries. Proudly Truman told the world that it had been only seven years since America first exploded an atom bomb in the New Mexico desert. Now we would soon demonstrate what could become an important application of that awesome power. The President said:

"The engine of the *Nautilus* will have as revolutionary effect on the navies of the world as did the first ocean steamship 120 years ago." (He must have referred to Samuel Cunard's *Royal William*.)

A few weeks after the keel-laying, Rickover received a medal. Rather, it was a gold star in lieu of a second Legion of Merit. He had first received this high honor during World War II. The gold star came on July 7, 1952. On July 8, the Navy Selection Board met again to pass on candidates for Admiral. Captain H. G. Rickover had been recommended strongly for three years by his own superior officers and also the AEC. President Truman had praised the *Nautilus*, and the second Legion of Merit also attested to Rickover's abilities. After considering all these things, however, the Board passed by Rickover for a second consecutive year, and two passovers meant automatic retirement. Rickover, with thirty years of splendid service behind him, was to be turned out to pasture at the early age of fifty-two.

Rickover faced a miserable future. If he was retired he knew many of his men would leave the project. Besides that was the awful knowledge that he wasn't wanted by the Navy. One development helped: whatever it thought of Rickover, the Navy had just let the contract for a second atomic sub, to be called the *Sea Wolf*.

The situation between Rickover and the Navy seemed impossible to solve. Much sympathy—that of Congress, business, and the public, was with the captain who had been twice passed over. The Navy could not reverse the decision of its Selection Board; however, Rickover was asked to stay on despite the regulation that a twice passed-over officer be retired. The reason: there was no one to replace him. He stayed, and work went on with the *Nautilus*.

In July of 1953, when his name came up a third time, Rickover was finally made an Admiral. A year later, the atomic submarine was triumphantly launched. Its career has been spectacularly successful. By January of 1955 the *U.S.S. Nautilus* (*SSN-571*) was cruising submerged on atomic power. On her shakedown voyage she traveled from New London, Connecticut, all the way to San Juan, Puerto Rico, submerged. She was down for eighty-four hours on the 1300-mile trip, setting new records for distance and speed. Before the old-time sub shippers recovered from that, *Nautilus* submerged for 265 hours and turned in an average speed of almost twenty knots. Every other sub in the world was suddenly outmoded.

Within two years of her maiden trip *Nautilus* had covered the twenty thousand leagues under the sea of Jules Verne's fictional submarine. It had not drawn its power from the sea, as Verne's craft did, but it had traveled the sixty thousand miles on a nuclear charge about the size of a golf ball. To travel an equal distance, a conventional sub's engines would burn up ninety tank cars of oil!

In 1958 *Nautilus* was the first submarine to cruise from the Pacific to the Atlantic under the polar ice. Its atomic engine gave it the ability to cruise under water so long that it has been jokingly said it surfaces only to permit the crew to re-enlist. Of course, like the early steamboats that carried sail as a precaution, *Nautilus* has diesel and electric engines also as a safety measure.

In January of 1957 the *Sea Wolf* was launched. Its engine was the liquid-metal type advocated by General Electric, but it was soon replaced with a water engine like that Rickover favored for the *Nautilus*. Since then there have been dozens of nuclear subs launched by the Navy, including many of the *Polaris* nuclear missile launchers.

The Navy has also built an atomic aircraft carrier, a cruiser, and a destroyer. But it is the submarine, the *true* submarine dreamt of by Jules Verne and others that was brought to reality mainly by the perseverance of one man —Admiral H. G. Rickover. His pioneering work led to another kind of atomic vessel in the merchant ship *Savannah*.

· *Savannah*

In 1955, with the *Nautilus* a success, President Eisenhower ordered a merchant ship to be started, powered by atomic energy. It would be called the *Savannah*, for the first ship that crossed the Atlantic, in 1819, partially on steam power. This new *Savannah* was to be of twenty-two thousand tons displacement, and carry sixty passengers and a cargo of ten thousand tons. Although it would cost some 50 per cent more than a conventional craft, its atomic power plant was to give a cruising range of 300,000 miles without refueling. Savannah was designed to travel a dozen times around the world at its top speed of thirty knots and burn only 110 pounds of uranium. A conventional ship would burn more than 100,000 tons of fuel oil!

Before building *Savannah*, the Maritime Service ordered a test hull called the *Atomic Servant* to try out the atomic power plant. Then work got under way on the pioneer craft itself. When it was finished it was a proud and beautiful ship. Perhaps the most modern ship afloat, the *Savannah* had a specially trained crew who wore a unique insignia designating the power their craft used. Gyro stabilizers insured a smooth ride, and passenger cabins and lounges were palatial. Long cruises were planned to show the world the new wonder of the seas. Yet, with all this in its favor, the new *Savannah* came to grief much as had its predecessor 140 years earlier.

No sooner was the ship completed and tested than labor problems beset her. The crew went on strike for better conditions and higher pay. Technical problems plagued her, too. In 1963, with the *Savannah* still not living up to her promise, there was a scathing article calling the ship a flop. She had taken two years longer than scheduled to build, it was charged, and cost $80 million, nearly twice the original estimate. Far from cruising 300,000 miles, her reactor had to be opened and repaired after only five months of intermittent operation. The gleaming *Savannah* had become a great white elephant of the sea-lanes. There was no rush to build another nuclear craft, although a tanker had been in the planning stage for years.

Today the atomic commercial ship stands about where the steamboat did in the first decade after Robert Fulton proved his *Clermont* could outdo the sailing ship. Apparently it is difficult to make a case for the economy of atomic power, unless high speed is admitted to be an advantage. And shippers ask who needs thirty knots? They claim that for the difference in price they are content with the twenty knots that conventional craft cruise at. To arguments that an atomic ship can cruise many times around the world without refueling, and with no need for shifting ballast as fuel is used up, they argue that *Savannah* is also a far greater hazard than an oil burner. Should there be an accident, passengers and crew might be wiped out. Suppose such an accident occurred in New York Harbor?

Even in the Navy, where atomic subs and surface craft have proved themselves, there is difficulty in convincing the administration to build more carriers and other craft. Here is an amazing paradox; the ship of the future is here, and there are few takers. In time, surely its worth will be realized, just as was the worth of steam and metal hulls. Some day a brave ship line will order fast atomic passenger ships that may even win some passengers back from the airlines. At worst, war, or the threat of it, will prove that failing to build atomic craft is the falsest economy. Then atomic power will have come of age.

"Nimble thought can jump both sea and land."

—William Shakespeare,
Sonnet 44

7

Christopher Cockerell and His Hovercraft

HOVERCRAFT: *a vehicle that rides on an air cushion created by a lifting propeller or ducted fan.*

About the same time that Captain Rickover was urging the atomic submarine for the U. S. Navy, a lean, bespectacled engineer in England was trying to create some interest in a ship even more startling. This man was Christopher Cockerell, and the reason his "ship" jolted the doubters even more than the atomic power concept was because it floated not *on* the water, but some distance *above* it. This strange new ship was the "hovercraft."

It took Cockerell some time to get into production with his hovercraft, but once it got off the water in the late 1950's things happened fast. One British firm has produced and sold twenty such craft—at prices of more than \$1 million each—and British hovercraft have invaded America. Dozens of other boats that ride a cushion of air have been produced by firms in England, America, Russia, Finland, Sweden, and elsewhere. Such craft, often called "ground-effect machines" or GEM's, range from do-it-yourself kits for several hundred dollars, to multi-passenger transports and large military craft.

All inventions stem from a need, and the need for the hovercraft was apparent in several different aspects. Speed is one factor. The resistance of a craft's hull consumes great amounts of power, and the faster it pushes through the water the less efficiently is its power used. The answer was to get the hull *out* of the water somehow. Conventional marine architects tried this with clever "stepped" hulls in which the craft rose partially out of the water as it attained speed. But the hovercraft completely leaves its watery domain and becomes to all intents an aircraft flying at an extremely low altitude.

It is possible, of course, to drive a more or less conventional hull through the water at hundreds of miles an hour; Sir Donald Campbell has bettered 275 mph in a racing hydroplane. However, the increase in hull resistance just from fifty knots to one hundred knots is prohibitive for all but racing craft or perhaps military vessels. The same condition prevails with aircraft. A light plane will fly at one hundred miles an hour with good engine efficiency; at two hundred miles an hour it requires far more than double the amount of fuel per mile. But wind resistance is relatively much less than water resistance, and so the hovercraft can attain speeds of around one hundred miles an hour with little penalty.

There are other advantages, including smoothness of ride and safety. An airplane crash-landing at sea is not the safest thing to be aboard. But hovercraft have demonstrated that there is little problem in "ditching" from a couple of feet above the waves. There is another advantage indicating that the hovercraft is an evolutionary step in transportation; it can float over not only water, but ice, snow, mud, or dry land with equal ability. We have seen that the hovercraft is a kind of hybrid boat-airplane. It also is either a boat that sails on land, or a land vehicle that can go to sea. Docking facilities are not needed, and the amphibian qualities of the hovercraft make transferring from train or bus to boat and back unnecessary, where it is advantageous to make the trip in one vehicle. There is the feeling among its proponents, then, that the new craft has in one fell swoop outmoded not only the keel but the wheel as well.

· *Early Hovercraft*

The atomic-powered ship is quite obviously of recent origin. This is not the case with the hovercraft, or air-cushion vehicle. In 1849 the American steamer *John Neilson* was fitted with a device to force air under the bottom of the hull as the vessel moved through the water. The modified steamer achieved a speed of twenty miles an hour, an accomplishment for those days. This was not a hovercraft, of course, but the idea would be a take-off point for the man who a century later produced the first practical craft of that type.

The sport of "skipping" stones across the water is nothing new, doubtless having been practiced for hundreds or thousands of years. Perhaps this skimming flight of the flat stone above the water inspired an inventive Frenchman named Mâle. In 1881 Monsieur Mâle suggested a boat that would ride on a cushion of air atop the surface of the water. Eight years later an American named Culbertson patented such a craft in this country. This was in the days of James Rumsey's strange water-jet craft, and John Fitch's early attempts at steam power. Culbertson's pioneer hovercraft seems to have made no impression, and perhaps a working model was never built.

For decades inventors neglected the idea of sailing on a cushion of air, except with airplanes, of which the air was increasingly full after December, 1903. It was not until 1935 that a Finn named Kaario built what seems the first successful marine hovercraft. This primitive vehicle flew or sailed over water, ice, and mud but it, too, remained simply an interesting curiosity as far as most marine designers were concerned. After all, how seriously could you take a boat that did not ride *in* the water?

· Christopher Cockerell

Christopher Cockerell, the man who would take ships out of the water, was born in 1910. His father was Sir Sydney Cockerell, curator of the Fitzwilliam Museum in Cambridge, England. As a boy, Cockerell favored mechanical things over his more classical studies and one of his first projects was attaching a steam engine to his mother's sewing machine. Quite naturally, when it was time for college, he studied engineering at Cambridge.

He specialized in electrical and electronic engineering, and upon graduation went to work for the British Marconi radio firm. By World War II he was head of a team developing a radio-direction-finding system for the RAF. Another project was long-range television transmission. But in 1950 the forty-year-old engineer left Marconi and went into a completely new venture—that of boatbuilding.

There were many boatbuilders, but Cockerell had some ideas for better boats. First, he experimented with the old idea of pumping a thin layer of air beneath the hull of his small craft. As he had hoped, this lessened the water resistance and boosted the speed of the boat. The mechanism for doing this job of streamlining of the water about the boat consisted of an old vacuum cleaner and a fan he purchased at a junkshop.

Thus far Cockerell was applying to his boats an idea something like one that aircraft designers had long been interested in. This was "laminar" flow, or keeping the flow in smooth layers rather than a boiling turbulence around the flight surfaces. Cockerell now began to think of a more startling idea, that of trapping a thick cushion of air beneath the boat. It was a good idea, and one that others had tried before him.

The theory of the hovercraft is simple. A parachute slows a jumper by trapping and slightly compressing air within its nylon canopy. A helicopter can support more weight near the ground because of the "ground-effect" in which the stream of air strikes the earth and is compressed.

The ground cushion makes the landing of conventional aircraft easier, too. This was what Cockerell wanted to put to work on his boat; but it was difficult to keep the air from spilling out as fast as his compressor pumped it to the chamber beneath the craft. Again he resorted to homely equipment and solved the problem—with two tin cans! Nesting a smaller can in a larger, the inventor pumped air through a hole in the top of the outer can. The resulting curtain or ring of air trapped a cushion of air inside it and the crude model Cockerell had built lifted from the floor with very little power.

By now it was 1953. Cockerell was sure he had something, but he lacked the money to properly develop his hovercraft idea. He applied for a patent and sought help. Government agencies spent three years deciding that while the hovercraft was an interesting toy it had no practical military or commercial applications. However, during this time a few men had become interested in the idea of a boat that floated above the waves and a small sum of money was made available. Finally, the National Research Development Corporation offered to back the inventor. The aircraft firm of Saunders-Roe was commissioned to build the *SRN-1*, and in June of 1959 the first English hovercraft was launched. It created an immediate sensation.

The hovercraft was a weird vessel as it went through its paces. Thirty feet long and a broad twenty-four feet across, the *SRN-1* resembled a squat tug with a huge smokestack amidships. The smokestack was actually a fan that forced air into a cushion beneath the craft. While the engine roared noisily the *SRN-1* lifted a foot or so from the water in a churning of spray and cruised about the

Thames as no other vessel had ever done. It could turn in
its own length, and even climb up the shallow ramp onto
dry land instead of tying up at a dock. Ungainly as it
looked, the hovercraft could skim over the water at fifty
knots!

When skeptics called the demonstration a stunt, the
SRN-1 loaded aboard twenty combat-equipped Royal Ma-
rines and performed well. Later it crossed the English
Channel, to the consternation of the government officials
who had seen no use for such a vessel. The *SRN-1* was admittedly only an experimental craft; Saunders-Roe was already building the improved *SRN-2*, and had plans for
others.

The impression the hovercraft made on the world was
great and immediate. Within a year there were a dozen
other craft built or building in England. In Finland, inventor Kaario built a hovercraft at the Valmet Company.
A Swiss inventor named Carl Weiland was flying a large
hovercraft of his own design on Lake Constance. And in
the United States an estimated sixty companies were busy
on hovercraft!

The U. S. Maritime Commission, busy with the revolutionary *Savannah* atom ship, began talking of a giant
ocean-going GEM named *Columbia*. The Office of Naval
Research had commissioned several contractors to go to
work on cushion craft. The Bureau of Naval Weapons had
Convair designing large hovercraft of circular shape. The
Bureau of Ships put the Hughes and Martin airplane companies to work on hovercraft. Bell Aircraft was busy with
what would become the *Hydroskimmer* for the Navy.

Private individuals, too, were developing small craft.

Among these was Dr. William Bertelsen of Neoponset, Illinois, who built his *Aeromobile* at home for a cost of about $600. It skimmed across rivers and fields at sixty miles an hour, flying about six inches high.

A larger craft, operating in America the same year that Cockerell's hovercraft flew in England was the *Air Car* of the Curtiss-Wright Corporation. This four-passenger twenty-one-foot car was powered by a three-hundred-horsepower engine and attained sixty miles an hour over land or water.

England and Cockerell continued to lead the way, however. The firm of Vickers Armstrong was also building versions of Cockerell's invention, and by 1962 its *VA-3* inaugurated ferry service across the Dee estuary from Rhyl, Wales, to the resort of Wallasey in Cheshire, England. Because of the shallow water and shifting sand banks, conventional ferry service had never been possible. A roundabout train trip takes about two hours; the *VA-3* made the crossing in just nineteen minutes. The train fare was $2.25; hovercraft passengers paid $2.80 for the quicker trip.

The *VA-3* was powered by four engines, two of them providing the cushion of air nine inches thick beneath the craft, and the other two driving it at a top speed of sixty-eight miles per hour. The twelve-ton craft carried a full load of sixty-four passengers on its maiden voyage, or flight; no one seemed sure whether it sailed or flew. The operators of the new ferry were pleased with passenger reaction. The craft was noisy, as they already knew. Another complaint was that there "really ought to be a toilet!" But there were no serious faults found with the new transportation method.

Soon after the Dee estuary run was made, an eighty-eight-passenger service was started across the Thames River. Planned also was similar service across the English Channel to the continent in twenty minutes.

Meantime, Westland Aircraft was building advanced hovercraft. The *SRN-2* was a twenty-seven-ton craft carrying twenty-four passengers at seventy knots, and the *SRN-3* was ten tons heavier. The first very large hovercraft will be the *SRN-4*, planned for about 150 tons. But first a small *SRN-5* weighing only seven tons was built and found very successful. It featured the addition of "skirts" around the sides of the hull to retain more of the air cushion. Carrying a pilot and four passengers, the *SRN-5* found a ready market.

A variation of the skirt idea was used in another craft built by an English firm named Denny. Not strictly a hovercraft, the Denny boat was fitted with skirts that dipped *below* the surface of the water, and was powered by an underwater propeller to lessen the noise. Obviously such a craft cannot run up onto dry land, and is strictly a seagoing vessel.

The height the hovercraft flies above the water is a limiting factor in its performance. Early craft flew a foot or so above the surface, and thus could not negotiate high waves. On the Dee estuary run, for example, it was necessary to halt operation when waves reached three feet in height. As larger hovercraft are built they will rise higher above the surface, since this height is a function of the diameter of the craft itself. Envisioned are hovercraft flying as much as fifteen feet over the water.

The cushion height is important for land operations, too, and the climbing of grades. Dr. Bertelsen's tiny *Aeromobile* stubbed its toes on slight obstructions. But the skirt idea is helpful in this respect and hill-climbing, or wave-riding hovercraft seem probable. The original *SRN-1* could successfully climb an 8 per cent grade, incidentally.

Now that we have seen the splash the hovercraft made when it first dunked itself in the Thames, let's see what is ahead for the new craft, from tiny one-man vehicles built of old lawnmowers and vacuum cleaners to giant atomic-powered dream ships hundreds of feet in diameter.

· *The Hovercraft's Future*

Development of air-cushion craft in America progressed rapidly once Cockerell's *SRN-1* had proved itself. Dr. Bertelsen soon had an improved *Aeromobile* whizzing across the ice-jammed Mississippi at seventy miles an hour, stopping for a landing in the river just to show how easy it was. Carl Weiland's design for an *Everglades Speedster* was translated into a four-passenger craft plying the Ohio River at Louisville at a seventy-five-mile-an-hour clip. Bell's *Hydroskimmer* Navy craft was operating on Lake Erie by 1963. Scientists at Princeton University rode about on their air-cushion craft, fitted with handlebars like an airborne motorcycle. And the Dobson *Airdart* was offered for sale complete or as a kit a handyman could put together at home.

The air-cushion principle had far more uses than as a

flying boat. A new model vacuum cleaner rides a cushion of air for less resistance, and the same idea was put to work on a device for moving heavy loads around in factories. Such a lift truck can be handled easily, moving without friction in all directions. Another land-borne application is the air-cushion lawn mower that literally flies through the job.

Although it is on the water that the hovercraft finds its most important uses, much of the work has been done by aircraft firms. This is quite natural, since the hovercraft is to all intents "an aircraft operating in close proximity to the surface." In 1961 Donald Douglas, president of Douglas Aircraft, suggested hovercraft of up to one thousand tons displacement for use as military craft and commercial vessels. Somewhat more costly to operate than conventional ships, they would, however, cruise at speeds four or five times as fast for deluxe passenger service, delivery of perishable cargoes, or for mail or military service. And their operation cost would be about half that of a helicopter.

As a military landing craft capable of sweeping ashore in the surf and running right up on the beach, the advantages of the hovercraft are obvious. Less obvious is the fact that since a hovercraft rides above the water and transmits no noise to the water, detection by a submarine would be almost impossible. Another proposed use of the hovercraft is as a carrier for missiles and rockets from factory to launch site, a job now done by conventional boat, rail, truck, or sometimes even by airplane.

Inventor Cockerell sees the hovercraft not as a compromise or combination of boat and airplane and car, but as a completely new method of transportation. It cannot compete with jet aircraft, at six hundred miles per hour but where there is a need for speedy overwater transport in the range of 100 to 150 knots, the hovercraft will make a place for itself. An ocean crossing in a single day instead of the four days in conventional liners should appeal. The hovercraft also makes navigable many shallow and obstacle-filled waterways unusable at present. And it can render meaningless the once forbidden boundaries between land and water.

"Nothing of him that doth fade
But doth suffer a sea-change
Into something rich and strange."

—William Shakespeare,
The Tempest

8

Of Other Ships

and Men

The desperate attempt by proponents of sail to save the day for their gallant craft led to some clever inventions. As early as 1850, one Henry Cunningham patented a "reefing gear" for handling sails from the deck instead of having to climb aloft. His gear made it possible for "one man and a boy" to close-reef a sail in heavy weather in only a few seconds. Good as this idea was, it was futile, as was the "steam-operated" sailing ship. A concession to the movement from sail to steam was a seven-masted sailing ship, *Thomas Larson.* Seven masts would have been enough to thoroughly cow the oldtime sailor, but the new ship used steam engines —not to drive her through the water, but to handle the sails. It was a humane idea, and it lessened the size of the crew. This latter was providential, for it spared some lives when the *Thomas Larson* sank with nearly all her crew off the Scilly Islands in 1902.

Even then, the sailing ship was not yet through. In the 1920's inventor Anton Flettner, who had created the famous Flettner rudder for easier steering of steamships, powered two big German ships by "rotors." The rotor is a spinning cylinder that creates lift when wind passes over it; a phenomenon evidenced by a baseball that curves when the proper spin is applied by the pitcher.

Flettner refitted the sailing ship *Buckner* with rotors operated by engines to prove the rotorship was a workable and perhaps even practical craft. It was safer in a gale and more maneuverable than its sail-rigged predecessors. Next a specially designed rotorship, the *Barbara*, was built, and for a time it seemed that this modernized sailing vessel might be able to compete with steam. A host of technical problems finally whipped the gallant German craft, although not before Flettner had also tried a weird windmill-driven boat!

The defeat of sails by steam would seem to end the fight for new kinds of craft, but such has not been the case at all. Instead the rash of inventions afloat has apparently increased, now that it seems unwise to devote more time to exploiting the wind as such. In the first chapter we pointed out that shipbuilding progressed very slowly for ten thousand years, and then accelerated in the last century and a half. Now, instead of slowing down, the flood of radical ideas is increasing even more, despite the obvious conclusion that there must be an end to freak craft somewhere.

The dictionary defines a boat as a small open vessel propelled by sails or oars; a ship is any seagoing vessel larger than a boat. While this wording is a bit confusing, any seafaring man can tell you what boats and ships are—or rather he could until recently. Today the nautical world is undergoing a sea change the likes of which Will Shakespeare never dreamed, and many an old salt heads for the safety of dry land. Well he might, when he sees the strange flotilla of weird craft that no longer merely float but fly, skim, hover, loop-the-loop, flip, walk, and even just plain *sink* into the water. Going down to the sea in ships today calls for more than just a watertight hull, and if all a craft will do is float, its designer had best hasten back to his drawing board. The watery revolution is on, and the results are amazing.

Instead of conventional craft, the sea is dotted with "bathyscaphes," "hydro-skimmers," "aqua-jets," "submarine planes," and "hydrofoils." We have everything from "swamp buggies" that roll across the water to "skinless diver" robots and "hydrocopters." This is a strange new breed of nautical craft.

· Bathyscaphe: The Ocean-going Balloon

Submarines were not new in 1948 but that was the year Swiss scientist Auguste Piccard had invented a weird new kind of craft for exploring the bottom of the sea. No simple submarine, his "bathyscaphe" was actually a misguided balloon, designed to sink to the bottom of the sea, and return to its surface. The "gasbag" from which hangs the gondola for the crew, contains not gas but gasoline— twenty-eight thousand gallons of it. This liquid is lighter than water and so it supports the weight of the bathyscaphe. Thus it differs entirely from William Beebe's "bathysphere," a steel ball that hung from a cable.

Water is admitted to the flotation compartments in the bathyscaphe and the craft sinks slowly into the sea. Since gasoline and water do not mix, the gasoline rises to the top. Electric power provides slow movement for the undersea craft to accomplish its explorations, and iron pellets are used for ballast. Dropping these lets the bathyscaphe return to the surface, and in the event of a power failure the ballast is dropped automatically since it is held in place by electromagnets. This gives the bathyscaphe a "fail-safe" feature that must be comforting to its passengers.

Piccard's strange craft reached a depth of 1500 meters, or nearly a mile, in 1948. Later, the French Navy took over the bathyscaphe and by 1958 it had reached 4100 meters, or about two and a half miles. Meantime, Piccard built a second, improved bathyscaphe which he named *Trieste*. His son Jacques, following in his famous father's footsteps, piloted *Trieste* 3700 meters below the Tyrrhenian Sea in what was but a prelude to a new low in oceanic exploration. In 1958 the U. S. Navy acquired *Trieste*, basing it in San Diego, California. In January, 1960, Jacques Piccard and Navy Lieutenant Don Walsh took deep breaths and plunged down toward the Marianas Trench off Guam, the deepest known marine canyon in the world. Almost five hours later they reached the bottom at 10,096 meters—about seven miles deep! Pressure at this record depth was a crushing 16,883 pounds per square inch, compared with the approximately 15 pounds pressure we are accustomed to. Fortunately the stout three and a half inch steel walls of the gondola held. Since the record dive, *Trieste* has been further improved and now has a mechanical arm for scooping samples off the bottom.

Unlike aircraft altitude records, the distance that man can go below sea level is fixed—unless he is prepared to dig his way into the bottom of the sea. This doesn't seem to have stopped the building of undersea exploration craft, however. Inner space, as it is called, is a vital area of man's future, and much work is being planned for its careful study. Among the craft being built in America are the *Aluminaut* by Reynolds Metal Company, the *Mesoscaph* by Loral Electronics, and *Deepstar* by Westinghouse. *Mesoscaph* was designed by Jacques Piccard, and *Deepstar* by another famous underwater rover, Jacques-Yves Cousteau of skin diving fame.

Loral, incidentally, is already well known in the nautical world for its *Pegasus*, a kind of open-air—or open-water—submarine. This *Pegasus* is a seahorse designed by French undersea explorer Dr. Dimitri Rebikoff. More accurately it is called a submarine plane and is flown much like its airborne cousin. Dr. Rebikoff has even learned to loop and do other "hydrobatics," one of which is to jump completely out of the water, like a dolphin at Marineland. There are some other weird craft that do their flying mostly out of the water.

• *Hydrofoil: The Ship That Flies through the Water*

For thousands of years, man has been quite happy with the density of the water his boats floated upon, knowing that this kept him from sinking to the bottom. More recently, as speed became of more importance, he realized that the resistance, or drag of the water, was using up most of his propulsive power.

Commercial ship lines and, of course, the military, have expended much thought and money in efforts to push ever faster through the water. Since the porpoise slips through the sea at a high rate of speed, his motions and even his skin, have been carefully studied and copied in an attempt to emulate his rapidity. Paint that would copy the yielding quality of porpoise skin is the dream of many a marine engineer, and perhaps someday such an approach will prove fruitful. Meantime, another development has come along which permits man to enjoy the advantages of water travel and eliminate one of the big disadvantages.

It has been known for a long time that if the drag of the hull could be eliminated the craft would move faster. Water is about eight hundred times as dense as the air above it. Racing hydroplanes get up "on the step" and thus attain their fabulous speeds, but to do this with a huge cargo carrier is obviously impossible. The wings of a seaplane lift the hull clear of the water, but this is too much of a good thing. Boats have been fitted with air wings to partially lift them out of the water, but such a craft is awkward to moor. The wing idea was a good one, however, and just as Da Vinci's propeller was appropriated by John Ericsson in 1836, the wings of the Wrights and others were borrowed by boat designers for underwater use as early as 1905! In that year an Italian named Enrico Forlanini built a crude hydrofoil boat and sailed or flew it on Lake Maggiore. It happened that there was an American named Alexander

Graham Bell among those watching the strange-winged boat, and while Bell is better known for inventing the telephone, he also designed and built the first American hydrofoil. He produced a number of these revolutionary craft, and in 1919 his *HD-4*, powered by two Liberty engines, set a world speed record of more than seventy miles an hour.

Despite the apparent success of Bell's hydrofoils, there were problems of stability, and his revolutionary craft made no great splash in American waters. For decades, then, there was no interest in the United States in wings for boats. In Germany, however, Hans von Schertel began in 1927 to experiment with hydrofoils. By 1944, when the Allies began to close in on Hitler, the Germans were planning high-speed attack vessels as large as eighty tons using hydrofoils.

After the war, von Schertel went to Switzerland and worked with an association which produced the *Supramar* —or "over the sea" hydrofoil boats. Today these vessels ply the waters in the Straits of Messina and also between Bellingham, Washington, and Vancouver, B.C., and in the Philippine Islands. There are perhaps two dozen hydrofoil boats operating commercially. A number of American firms are now active in the hydrofoil field, among them, interestingly, two of the large aircraft companies—Boeing and Grumman. They have built large vessels for the Navy, both military and transport craft.

Simple as was the idea of the wing that flies through the water, its perfection was very difficult. Besides the problem of stability that licked Bell decades ago, there are others like turbulence, or "cavitation" as it is called, about the submerged wing. This phenomenon is something like the pile-up of molecules on an airplane wing causing drag, but compounded by the increased density of water as compared with air. The problem has been solved by so-called "super-cavitating" foils, in which the wing surface is surrounded almost completely by a vapor cavity to lessen drag.

There are two main types of foils, the penetrating foil, and the completely submerged foil. With both types, increasing speed lifts the hull itself from the water. In the case of the ninety-ton hydrofoil ship *H. S. Denison*, built by Grumman for the U. S. Maritime Administration, the hull "flies" at sixty-three knots five feet above the water on penetrating foils! Boeing's one-hundred-and-ten-ton *High Point* Navy patrol boat uses fully submerged foils to attain a speed of fifty knots. Its hull-borne speed is only twelve knots. Hydrofoils in Italy have operated successfully in sixteen-foot waves, planing up one side and down the other. Of course, when really heavy seas are encountered, the hydrofoil meekly sets down on its hull.

Some of the big hydrofoils are taxied through the water by jet engines, in which water is pumped out the rear much like the pioneer steamship of Rumsey back in 1786! Boeing has a design nicknamed "Little Squirt" in which the jet is ejected *above* water. Borrowing from the aerodynamicist, some hydrofoil designers use aircraft propellors to drive their craft. Foils are retractable in some cases, to simplify mooring and also cleaning the foil of barnacles and other growths which would reduce its efficiency. Small kits are offered to pleasure boat owners, some for less than

$300, which boost the speed of the craft to thirty-five knots with an engine of about thirty-five horsepower. Even sailboats have been equipped with foils.

The advantages of the hydrofoil are many. First, of course, is speed and economy because there is less drag and no bow wave to fight. Next is the smooth ride. Flying atop the waves eliminates the jouncing of choppy seas; it is felt that there will be less seasickness in hydrofoils. In making turns, the hydrofoil boat does not slip as much as its conventional cousin, since the foils grip the water for tighter turns. Apparently the hydrofoils are safe, too, as tests have proved they will cut their way through small obstructions easily. In case of heavy objects, however, the foils will shear away from the hull. Obviously the hydrofoil boat will not be practical in iceberg waters.

· RUM: The Remote Underwater Manipulator

Even *Trieste, Aluminaut,* and other manned craft are part robot in that they have remote-controlled "prosthetic" arms to scoop things from the ocean floor. Denizens of the sea must look with wonder on this new breed; part man, part fish, and part machine.

An interesting sidelight on the bathyscaphe was its unmanned first "flight." Designer Piccard wisely let the craft travel alone by remote control on early trips. The idea of the robot boat—or perhaps the "roboat"—has persisted and a recent example is called RUM, a quite nautical acronym for Remote Underwater Manipulator. Built for the Navy by the Scripps Institution of Oceanography, RUM is a robot that walks the sea bottom. Fitted with mechanical arms and electronic eyes and ears, the manipulator trundles into the sea and waddles out to depths of 1500 feet.

More recently Hughes Aircraft Company has built undersea "mobots," or mobile robots, and one is in use by Shell Oil Company in its offshore oil drilling research. Called APE, this "skinless diver" is doubtless the forerunner of a family of undersea robots. APE may even sprout wings and become a "hydrocopter," according to Hughes.

· *The Ship That Flipped*

In addition to its RUM, the Navy has another strange craft called FLIP, an abbreviation for Floating Instrument Platform. Designed by Scripps, it is perhaps the only ship in the world that puts out to sea with its bunks on vertical walls, and gear hanging from the ceiling. It is surely the only vessel with a draft of three hundred feet! A powerless craft 355 feet long, FLIP does just what its name suggests when it has been towed to its proper station in the Pacific. The aft sections of the tubular giant with the rounded prow are intentionally flooded and the craft literally "flips." Riding vertically, with fifty-five feet of its bow out of the water, the crew's bunks and other facilities at last are in the position they should be, and FLIP becomes a marine laboratory into whose depths scientists can descend to study ocean currents, noises, temperatures, and other factors.

Electronic gear permits research of underwater sound propagation, for FLIP's first mission is to aid in undersea warfare studies. Later it will work for the marine biologist and oceanographer with research on plant and animal growth, wave research, and so on. Another similar craft, aptly named SPAR because that's what it looks like, was designed for the same sort of tasks in the Atlantic.

· *The Flying Submarine*

There is perhaps no end to the new ideas inventors will come up with for seagoing craft, but the flying submarine will have to be the last strange craft we discuss. Sounding like something out of Tom Swift, or a marine architect's nightmare, such craft are actually on the drawing boards. Sponsored by the U. S. Navy's Airframe Design Division, General Dynamics/Convair has made a six-months study of a craft capable of flying through the air at better than two hundred miles per hour, and also cruising underwater at five knots and a depth of seventy-five feet for fifty nautical miles!

Weighing about eight tons, the flying sub would carry a crew of two and be powered by three jet engines. Takeoffs and landings would use "hydro-skis." General Dynamics is a logical builder of such a weird underseaplane, since its Electric Boat Company has built not only Holland's pioneer subs and modern atomic submarines, but also the Navy's experimental "Sea Dart" aircraft which used the hydro-ski landing gear.

The Air Force, too, is interested in a submersible aircraft, and has commissioned the Rand Corporation to make studies of a strategic version of a flying submarine. Also planned are even stranger "deep-diving ballistic missiles."

Man, it seems, is determined to find new ways to go down to the sea. It is straining a point to call some of these new craft ships, but whatever they are, the men who design and build them will continue to be a strange and wonderful breed.

Today we have glass-bottomed boats and shoes that walk on the water. It has even been suggested that the electrical potential existing in the sea might be tapped to drive boats and ships through it. Yet, instead of shocking those associated with the new breed of nautical craft these days, such an idea is greeted with the comment, "It's about time somebody got around to that." After all, Jules Verne used that idea in his fictional tale of the *Nautilus!*

Index